Instructor's Resource Manual

Introductory Algebra
Eleventh Edition

Marvin Bittinger
Indiana University Purdue University Indianapolis

Addison-Wesley
is an imprint of

PEARSON

The author and publisher of this book have used their best efforts in preparing this book. These efforts include the development, research, and testing of the theories and programs to determine their effectiveness. The author and publisher make no warranty of any kind, expressed or implied, with regard to these programs or the documentation contained in this book. The author and publisher shall not be liable in any event for incidental or consequential damages in connection with, or arising out of, the furnishing, performance, or use of these programs.

Reproduced by Addison-Wesley from electronic files supplied by the author.

Copyright © 2011, 2007, 2003 Pearson Education, Inc.
Publishing as Pearson Addison-Wesley, 75 Arlington Street, Boston, MA 02116.

ISBN-13: 978-0-321-64071-0
ISBN-10: 0-321-64071-3

1 2 3 4 5 6 BRR 14 13 12 11

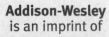

Addison-Wesley
is an imprint of

www.pearsonhighered.com

CONTENTS

INTRODUCTION

Dear Faculty:

The Bittinger book team at Pearson Arts & Sciences is very excited that you will be using *Introductory Algebra*, Eleventh Edition. We know that whether you are teaching this course for the first time or the tenth time, you will face many challenges, including how to prepare for class, how to make the most effective use of your class time, how to present the material to your students in a manner that will make sense to them, how best to assess your students, and the list goes on.

This manual is designed to make your job easier. Inside these pages are words of advice from experienced instructors, general and content-specific teaching tips, a list of the objectives covered within *Introductory Algebra*, descriptions of both student and instructor supplements that accompany this text, and a list of valuable resources provided by your fellow instructors.

We would like to thank the following professors for sharing their advice and teaching tips. This manual would not be what it is without their valuable contribution.

Chris Bendixen, *Lake Michigan College*

Endre Borsos, *Miami-Dade Community College, North Campus*

Gail G. Burkett, *Associate Professor of Mathematics, Palm Beach Community College*

William Graesser, *Ivy Tech State College*

Rosa Kavanaugh, *Division Chair/Instructor of Mathematics, Ozarks Technical Community College*

Roger McCoach, *County College Morris*

Dr. Deloria Nanze-Davis, *Chairperson of Mathematics at University of Texas at Brownsville and Texas Southmost College*

Jane Duncan Nesbit, *Columbia Union College*

Louise Olshan, *Professor of Mathematics, County College of Morris*

Tatiana Sviridovsky, *Assistant Professor of Mathematics, Delaware County Community College*

Sharon Testone, Ph.D., *Professor of Mathematics, Onondaga Community College*

Angela M. Walters, *Capitol College*

Roy D. West, *Robeson Community College*

Annette F. Wiesner, *University of Wisconsin-Parkside*

It is also important to know that you have a very valuable resource available to you in your Pearson Arts & Sciences sales representative. If you do not know your representative, you can locate him/her by logging on to Pearson www.pea/scnhighered.com/replocator and typing in your zip code. Please feel free to contact your representative if you have any questions relating to our text or if you need additional supplements.

We know that teaching this course can be challenging. We hope that this and the other resources we have provided will help to minimize the amount of time it takes you to meet those challenges.

Good luck in your endeavors!

The Bittinger book team

Dear Adjunct Faculty and Mentors:

My purpose in writing this introduction is to encourage both adjunct instructors and those responsible for guiding them to use the Instructor's Resource Manual. Adjunct faculty are playing an increasingly larger role in colleges and universities. At my institution adjunct faculty teach over 50% of the mathematics courses. In addition the adjunct's job is more challenging today than ever before. Some are hired on very short notice. Many drive from school to school, leaving them with very little preparation time. Still others receive little or no mentoring. With this confluence of an expanded role and increased difficulties, there comes a growing need to provide adjunct faculty with the support materials to help them meet a variety of challenges. The Instructor's Resource Manual is an invaluable resource in this regard.

This supplement has been developed by instructors for instructors. Virtually every element of the manual is the result of thoughtful comments and suggestions from adjunct faculty and their mentors. The offered recommendations address the challenges and concerns that adjunct faculty experience. Proposed topics range from the practical, such as items to be included in a syllabus in Sample Syllabi, to the probing, such as the most effective way to teach a particular concept in Teaching Tips Correlated to Textbook Sections. Other topics include General, First-Time Advice, and Helpful Tips for Using Supplements and Technology. As a result of faculty involvement, an extremely useful resource has been developed for all those engaged in the adjunct experience.

Whether you are an adjunct instructor or a supervisor of adjunct faculty, I hope my words will motivate you to use the tools found in this support manual. Developed by teachers for teachers and dealing with a variety of topics pertinent to the adjunct experience, I believe you will find the Instructor's Resource Manual a wonderful addition to the support materials published by Pearson Arts & Sciences.

Have a great semester!

John M. Samoylo
Mathematics Department Co-coordinator
Delaware County Community College

Factoring and LCMs

Learning Objectives:

    a   Find all the factors of numbers and find prime factorizations of numbers.
    b   Find the LCM of two or more numbers using prime factorizations.

Examples:

1. Find all the factors of each number.
    a) 30   b) 24   c) 45

2. Find the prime factorization of each number.
    a) 18   b) 49   c) 180

    d) 54   e) 12   f) 425

3. Find the LCM.
    a) 6, 7   b) 8, 12   c) 15, 45

    d) 18, 48   e) 2, 5, 11   f) 25, 35, 42

4. It takes Greg 6 min to jog around a track. It takes Tess 9 min to jog around the same track. If they start jogging at the same place and time, when will they next be together at the position where they started?

Teaching Notes:

- Point out that prime factorizations are unique if order is not considered.
- Make sure students can find LCMs using prime factorizations.

Answers: *1a) 1, 2, 3, 5, 6, 10, 15, 30, b) 1, 2, 3, 4, 6, 8, 12, 24, c) 1, 3, 5, 9, 15, 45; 2a) $2 \cdot 3 \cdot 3$, b) $7 \cdot 7$, c) $2 \cdot 2 \cdot 3 \cdot 3 \cdot 5$, d) $2 \cdot 3 \cdot 3 \cdot 3$, e) $2 \cdot 2 \cdot 3$, f) $5 \cdot 5 \cdot 17$; 3a) 42, b) 24, c) 45, d) 144, e) 110, f) 1050; 4) 18 min after they start*

Fraction Notation

Learning Objectives:

    a   Find equivalent fraction expressions by multiplying by 1.
    b   Simplify fraction notation.
    c   Add, subtract, multiply, and divide using fraction notation.

Examples:

1.   Write an equivalent expression for each of the fractions using the indicated name for 1.

    a) $\dfrac{2}{3}\left(\text{Use }\dfrac{4}{4}\text{ for 1.}\right)$
    b) $\dfrac{9}{11}\left(\text{Use }\dfrac{5}{5}\text{ for 1.}\right)$
    c) $\dfrac{5}{16}\left(\text{Use }\dfrac{10}{10}\text{ for 1.}\right)$

    d) $\dfrac{4}{5}\left(\text{Use }\dfrac{6}{6}\text{ for 1.}\right)$

2.   Simplify each fraction.

    a) $\dfrac{5}{10}$
    b) $\dfrac{42}{77}$
    c) $\dfrac{88}{90}$
    d) $\dfrac{5\cdot x}{15\cdot x}$

3.   Multiply. Simplify all answers.

    a) $\dfrac{5}{9}\cdot\dfrac{3}{15}$
    b) $\dfrac{5}{6}\cdot\dfrac{9}{2}$
    c) $\dfrac{4}{9}\cdot\dfrac{12}{13}$
    d) $\dfrac{4}{15}\cdot\dfrac{5}{12}$

4.   Divide. Simplify all answers.

    a) $\dfrac{5}{9}\div\dfrac{3}{15}$
    b) $\dfrac{5}{6}\div\dfrac{9}{2}$
    c) $\dfrac{5}{24}\div\dfrac{36}{24}$
    d) $\dfrac{3}{5}\div 20$

5.   Add or subtract. Simplify all answers.

    a) $\dfrac{3}{14}+\dfrac{4}{14}$
    b) $\dfrac{2}{3}-\dfrac{1}{3}$
    c) $\dfrac{2}{4}+\dfrac{1}{8}$
    d) $\dfrac{5}{6}+\dfrac{7}{8}$

    e) $\dfrac{7}{12}+\dfrac{9}{30}$
    f) $\dfrac{2}{3}+\dfrac{1}{6}$
    g) $\dfrac{5}{6}-\dfrac{1}{3}$
    h) $\dfrac{13}{16}-\dfrac{7}{12}$

Teaching Notes:

- Encourage students to simplify fractions by factoring into primes and removing factors of 1.
- Some students add/subtract the denominators when adding/subtracting fractions.

Answers: _1a)_ $\dfrac{8}{12}$, _b)_ $\dfrac{45}{55}$, _c)_ $\dfrac{50}{160}$, _d)_ $\dfrac{24}{30}$; _2a)_ $\dfrac{1}{2}$, _b)_ $\dfrac{6}{11}$, _c)_ $\dfrac{44}{45}$, _d)_ $\dfrac{1}{3}$; _3a)_ $\dfrac{1}{9}$, _b)_ $\dfrac{15}{4}$, _c)_ $\dfrac{16}{39}$, _d)_ $\dfrac{1}{9}$;

_4a)_ $\dfrac{25}{9}$, _b)_ $\dfrac{5}{27}$, _c)_ $\dfrac{5}{36}$, _d)_ $\dfrac{3}{100}$; _5a)_ $\dfrac{1}{2}$, _b)_ $\dfrac{1}{3}$, _c)_ $\dfrac{5}{8}$, _d)_ $\dfrac{41}{24}$, _e)_ $\dfrac{53}{60}$, _f)_ $\dfrac{5}{6}$, _g)_ $\dfrac{1}{2}$, _h)_ $\dfrac{11}{48}$

Decimal Notation

Learning Objectives:

    a   Convert from decimal notation to fraction notation.
    b   Add, subtract, multiply, and divide using decimal notation.
    c   Round numbers to a specified decimal place.

Examples:

1. Convert to fraction notation. Do not simplify.
   a) 0.3   b) 0.08   c) 3.25   d) 122.004

2. Convert to decimal notation.
   a) $\dfrac{7}{10}$ b) $\dfrac{1}{1000}$ c) $\dfrac{43}{100}$ d) $\dfrac{17}{10,000}$

3. Add or subtract.
   a) $56.3+12.2$ b) $1.665+9.888$ c) $48.7-2.9$ d) $30.44-16.3$

4. Multiply.
   a) 2.4×1.6 b) 0.581×2.9 c) 2.34×1000 d) 0.0343×100

5. Divide.
   a) $6\overline{)81.12}$ b) $2.6\overline{)54.6}$ c) $100\overline{)16,544}$ d) $0.38\overline{)1.615}$

6. Convert to decimal notation.
   a) $\dfrac{4}{5}$ b) $\dfrac{3}{8}$ c) $\dfrac{8}{16}$ d) $\dfrac{5}{15}$

7. Round to the nearest hundredth, tenth, and one.
   a) 485.0743   b) 8.9546   c) $\dfrac{11}{3}$ d) $\dfrac{6}{11}$

Teaching Notes:

- Most students find adding, subtracting, and multiplying easy.
- Some students have trouble with dividing, especially when the divisor is a decimal.

Answers: *1a)* $\dfrac{3}{10}$, *b)* $\dfrac{8}{100}$, *c)* $\dfrac{325}{100}$, *d)* $\dfrac{122,004}{1000}$; *2a) 0.7, b) 0.001, c) 0.43, d) 0.0017; 3a) 68.5, b) 11.553, c) 45.8, d) 14.14; 4a) 3,84, b) 1.6849, c) 2340, d) 3.43; 5a) 13.52, b) 21, c) 165.44, d) 4.25; 6a) 0.8, b) 0.375, c) 0.5, d) 0.$\overline{3}$; 7a) 485.07, 485.1, 485, b) 8.95, 9.0, 9 c) 3.67, 3.7, 4, d) 0.55, 0.5, 1*

Percent Notation

Learning Objectives:

    a   Convert from percent notation to decimal notation.
    b   Convert from percent notation to fraction notation.
    c   Convert from decimal notation to percent notation.
    d   Convert from fraction notation to percent notation.

Examples:

1. Convert to decimal notation.
    a) 2%   b) 30%   c) 9.5%   d) 0.044%   e) 244.9%

2. Convert to fraction notation.
    a) 40%   b) 26.2%   c) 150%   d) 0.034%   e) 5%

3. Convert to percent notation.
    a) 0.25   b) 0.8   c) 0.0616   d) 3.33   e) 1.4

4. Convert to percent notation.
    a) $\dfrac{2}{3}$ b) $\dfrac{3}{4}$ c) $\dfrac{3}{10}$ d) $\dfrac{5}{8}$ e) $\dfrac{9}{5}$

5. Complete the table.

	Decimal Notation	Fraction Notation	Percent Notation
a)	0.47		
b)			16%
c)		$\dfrac{121}{100}$	

Teaching Note:

*   Some students remember which way to move the decimal easier if you remind them that, as in the alphabet, move right for **D**ecimal to **P**ercent, and left for **P**ercent to **D**ecimal.

Answers: *1a) 0.02, b) 0.3, c) 0.095, d) 0.00044, e) 2.449; 2a)* $\dfrac{40}{100}$*, b)* $\dfrac{262}{1000}$*, c)* $\dfrac{150}{100}$*, d)* $\dfrac{34}{100,000}$*, e)* $\dfrac{5}{100}$*;*

3a) 25%, b) 80%, c) 6.16%, d) 333%, e) 140%; 4a) 66.$\overline{6}$%, or 66$\dfrac{2}{3}$%, b) 75%, c) 30%, d) 62.5%, or 62$\dfrac{1}{2}$%,

e) 180%; 5a) $\dfrac{47}{100}$*, 47%, b) 0.16,* $\dfrac{16}{100}$ *or* $\dfrac{4}{25}$*, c) 1.21, 121%*

Exponential Notation and Order of Operations

Learning Objectives:

    a   Write exponential notation for a product.
    b   Evaluate exponential expressions.
    c   Simplify expressions using the rules for order of operations.

Examples:

1. Write exponential notation.
    a) $6 \times 6 \times 6 \times 6$ b) $15 \cdot 15$ c) $10 \cdot 10 \cdot 10$

2. Evaluate.
    a) 6^2 b) 3^4 c) $\left(\dfrac{3}{4}\right)^4$

3. Calculate.
    a) $4 - 8 \div 2$ b) $2^2 \cdot 3 - 3$ c) $10 - 3^2 + 2$

    d) $16 - 32 \div 2^3$ e) $6 + \dfrac{16 - 4}{2 + 2^2} - 2$ f) $24 \div \dfrac{3^2}{9 - 6} + 5$

    g) $2\big[3(4 - 2) + 4\big]$

Teaching Notes:

- Some students do not know how to say 3^2, or 2^3, or 5^4, etc., in words and need to see the words written.
- Students should be reminded to work from inside out when evaluating expressions with grouping symbols.
- Refer students to the order of operations chart in the text.

Answers: *1a)* 6^4, *b)* 15^2, *c)* 10^3 ; *2a) 36, b) 81, c)* $\dfrac{81}{256}$; *3a) 0, b) 9, c) 3, d) 12, e) 6, f) 13, g) 20*

Geometry

Learning Objectives:

    a   Find the perimeter of a polygon.
    b   Find the area of a rectangle, a square, a parallelogram, and a triangle.
    c   Find the length of a radius of a circle given the length of a diameter, and find the length of a diameter given the length of a radius; find the circumference and the area of a circle.
    d   Find the volume of a rectangular solid.

Examples:

1. Find the perimeter and the area of the square that is 5 ft on a side.

2. Find the perimeter and the area of the rectangle that is 1.2 cm by 8 cm.

3. Find the perimeter of the polygon.

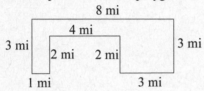

4. Find the area of each shape.
   a)

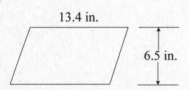

    b)

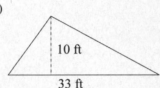

5. Find the diameter or radius of each circle, as appropriate.
   a) radius $r = 6.2$ cm   b) diameter $d = 49$ yd   c) diameter $d = 13.4$ in.

6. Find the circumference and area of each circle. Use 3.14 for π. Round to the nearest hundredth.
   a) radius = 12 cm   b) radius = 0.3 in.   c) diameter = 1.004 yd

7. Find the volume of the rectangular solid. Round to the nearest tenth.
   width = 1.3 ft, length = 4.5 ft, height = 3.1 ft

Teaching Notes:

- Some students have trouble remembering perimeter formulas. Remind them that they just need to remember that the perimeter is the sum of all the sides.
- Some students are unfamiliar with the concept of height with parallelograms and triangles.
- Encourage students to see the logic behind the area formulas.
- In finding area, some students need to be reminded to square the radius before multiplying by π.

Answers: *1a) 20 ft, 25 ft²; 2) 18.4 cm, 9.6 cm²; 3) 26 mi; 4a) 87.1 in², b) 165 ft²; 5a) diameter = 12.4 cm, b) radius = 24.5 yd, c) radius = 6.7 in.; 6a) circumference = 75.36 cm, area = 452.16 cm², b) circumference = 1.88 in., area = 0.28 in², c) circumference = 3.15 yd, area = 0.79 yd²; 7) 18.1 ft³*

Introduction to Algebra

Learning Objectives:

    a   Evaluate algebraic expressions by substitution.
    b   Translate phrases to algebraic expressions.

Examples:

1. Evaluate the expressions when $a = 2$, $b = 3$, and $c = 6$.

    a) $2a + 3b$

    b) $\dfrac{5(a+b)-1}{c}$

    c) $\dfrac{5ab}{6} + 3cb$

    d) $\dfrac{a+b^3-1}{7} + c$

2. Translate each phrase to an algebraic expression, using x as the variable.
    a) The quotient of 6 less than a number and 3.
    b) Fifty more than a number.
    c) The product of 8 and the sum of a number and 5.
    d) Thirteen less than three times a number.

3. Frank had \$100 before spending x dollars on a gift. How much money remains?

Teaching Notes:

- When a numerical coefficient is 1, the 1 is usually not written (e.g., $1x$ is usually written as x). Students often ignore a term when they do not see a coefficient.
- Remind students that an exponent refers only to the variable just before it (e.g., $5x^2$ means $5 \cdot x^2$, not $5x \cdot 5x$).
- Students often have difficulty translating phrases with "less than."
- Remind students that expressions evaluate to a number.

Answers: *1a) 13, b) 4, c) 59, d)10; 2a)* $\dfrac{x-6}{3}$*, b)* $x+50$*, c)* $8(x+5)$*, d)* $3x-13$*; 3) \$100 - x*

The Real Numbers

Learning Objectives:

  a   State the integer that corresponds to a real-world situation.
  b   Graph rational numbers on the number line.
  c   Convert from fraction notation for a rational number to decimal notation.
  d   Determine which of two real numbers is greater and indicate which, using < or >. Given an inequality like $a > b$, write another inequality with the same meaning. Determine whether an inequality like $-3 \le 5$ is true or false.
  e   Find the absolute value of a real number.

Examples:

1. State the integer that corresponds to the situation.
    a) Brent owes his parents $600.   b) Jayne has $125 in her checking account.

2. Graph each of the numbers on the number line: $-2,\ 5,\ -4\frac{1}{3},\ 1\frac{1}{2}$.

3. Convert to decimal notation.

    a) $-\dfrac{3}{4}$ b) $\dfrac{1}{6}$ c) $-\dfrac{3}{25}$

4. Use either < or > for $\square$ to write a true sentence.

    a) $-3\ \square\ 8$ b) $-\dfrac{4}{5}\ \square\ -\dfrac{1}{3}$ c) $10\ \square\ -12$

5. Write an inequality with the same meaning.
    a) $-6 \ge -10$ b) $-3 < 5$ c) $4 > 0$

6. Write true or false.
    a) $5 \ge 5$ b) $-3 \le -4$ c) $0 > -2$

7. Find the absolute value.
    a) $\left|-3\right|$ b) $\left|-6\right|$ c) $\left|4\right|$

Teaching Notes:

  • Remind students that integers are rational numbers; any integer can be written as the ratio of itself and 1.
  • Decimal numbers that terminate or repeat in a fixed block are both examples of rational numbers – ask students to give examples of both.
  • The decimal form of an irrational number neither terminates nor repeats.
  • Some students have never seen absolute value before and will need examples.

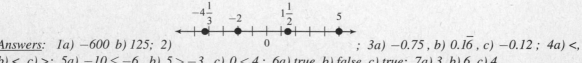

Answers: *1a) -600 b) 125; 2)*   *; 3a) -0.75, b) $0.1\overline{6}$, c) -0.12 ; 4a) <,*
b) <, c) >; 5a) $-10 \le -6$, b) $5 > -3$, c) $0 < 4$; 6a) true, b) false, c) true; 7a) 3, b) 6, c) 4

Addition of Real Numbers

Learning Objectives:

  a   Add real numbers without using the number line.
  b   Find the opposite, or additive inverse, of a real number.
  c   Solve applied problems involving addition of real numbers.

Examples:

1. Add.
    a) $9+12$

    b) $-16+(-10)$

    c) $-14+(-26)$

    d) $-6.3+5.2$

    e) $-12+(-6)+17$

    f) $-2+6+(-1)+7$

    g) $\dfrac{7}{10}+\left(-\dfrac{2}{5}\right)$

2. Find the opposite, or additive inverse.
    a) 6

    b) -5

    c) $-\dfrac{5}{6}$

3. Evaluate $-(-x)$ when:
    a) $x=-13$

    b) $x=5$

Solve each problem.

4. A scuba diver is at a depth of 16 ft below the surface. He descends another 8 ft. What is his new depth?

5. On January 14, in New Market, Indiana, the temperature rose $17°$ F in three hours. If the starting temperature was $-5°$ F, what was the temperature three hours later?

Teaching Notes:

  * Some students need to see addition problems done on the number line first.
  * Caution students about the difference between the subtract key and the change-of-sign key on a calculator.
  * Refer students to the summary box of rules for addition of real numbers.
  * The number line is a good way to illustrate opposite numbers – each equidistant from 0 but on opposite sides of 0.

Answers: 1a) 21, b) −26 , c) −40, d) −1.1, e) −1, f) 10, g) $\dfrac{3}{10}$; 2a) −6 , b) 5, c) $\dfrac{5}{6}$; 3a) −13 , b) 5;

4) −24 ft; 5) 12° F

Subtraction of Real Numbers

Learning Objectives:

    a   Subtract real numbers and simplify combinations of additions and subtractions.
    b   Solve applied problems involving subtraction of real numbers.

Examples:

1. Rewrite the following as addition problems using the definition of subtraction as addition of the opposite.
    a) $7-2$ b) $-3-6$ c) $13-(-1)$

2. Subtract.
    a) $3-7$ b) $-2-8$ c) $-6.3-(-4.1)$

3. Simplify.
    a) $-16-(-30)-12$ b) $14-8+19$ c) $-\dfrac{3}{4}+\dfrac{5}{8}-\left(-\dfrac{1}{2}\right)+\dfrac{17}{32}$

Solve each problem.

4. A scuba diver was at a depth of 17 ft below the surface. A wrecked ship was 12 ft lower than the diver. What was the depth of the wrecked ship?

5. The Terre Haute Golf Club showed a profit of $72,000 one year, while it had a loss of $19,000 in the next year. Find the difference between the amounts.

Teaching Notes:

- Many students find subtracting real numbers difficult at first.
- Some students forget to change the sign of the second number after changing subtraction to addition. Encourage students to show this step (e.g., $3-5=3+(-5)$).
- Make sure students understand the difference between the – symbol as it relates to subtraction, a negative number, or the opposite of a number.

Answers: *1a)* $7+(-2)$, *b)* $-3+(-6)$, *c)* $13+1$; *2a)* -4, *b)* -10, *c)* -2.2 ; *3a)* 2, *b)* 25, *c)* $\dfrac{29}{32}$; *4)* -29 *ft;* *5)* $91,000$

Multiplication of Real Numbers

Learning Objectives:

    a   Multiply real numbers.
    b   Solve applied problems involving multiplication of real numbers.

Examples:

1. Multiply.

    a) $-2(0)$ b) $4 \cdot (-15)$ c) $(-30)(-5)$ d) $(2.2)(-3.3)$ e) $\left(-\dfrac{3}{4}\right)\left(-\dfrac{5}{11}\right)$

2. Multiply.

    a) $-5 \cdot (-6) \cdot 2$ b) $4 \cdot (-3) \cdot 2 \cdot (-1) \cdot 0$ c) $(-1)^4$ d) $(-1)^7$

3. Evaluate the expression when $x = 4$.

    a) $(-5x)^2$ b) $-5x^2$

4. Evaluate the expression when $x = -3$.

    a) $(-x)^2$ b) $-x^2$

5. After diving 80 m below sea level, a diver rises at a rate of 6 m/min for 8 min. Where is the diver in relation to the surface at the end of the 8-min period?

Teaching Note:

- Refer students to the rules for multiplying real numbers.

Answers: *1a) 0, b) −60, c) 150, d) −7.26, e)* $\dfrac{15}{44}$ *; 2a) 60, b) 0, c) 1, d) −1; 3a) 400, b) −80; 4a) 9,*
b) −9; 5) −32 m

Division of Real Numbers

Learning Objectives:

    a   Divide integers.
    b   Find the reciprocal of a real number.
    c   Divide real numbers.
    d   Solve applied problems involving division of real numbers.

Examples:

1. Divide, if possible.

    a) $-16 \div 8$ b) $\dfrac{-9}{-3}$ c) $\dfrac{-46}{0}$ d) $\dfrac{0}{-4}$

2. Find the reciprocal.

    a) $\dfrac{5}{12}$ b) $\dfrac{1}{8}$ c) -6 d) $\dfrac{2}{3x}$

3. Rewrite each division as a multiplication.

    a) $3 \div 5$ b) $-\dfrac{2}{3} \div \left(-\dfrac{5}{8}\right)$ c) $\dfrac{n}{\frac{1}{p}}$

4. Divide, if possible.

    a) $-\dfrac{3}{5} \div \dfrac{15}{20}$ b) $-\dfrac{7}{8} \div \left(-\dfrac{3}{4}\right)$ c) $-22.5 \div 1.5$ d) $\dfrac{-8}{4-4}$

5. Last year, Perry's class had 2250 students. This year it has 2160 students. Find the change and the percent of increase or decrease from last year to this year.

Teaching Notes:

- Refer students to the rules for dividing real numbers.
- Give examples to show why division by zero is not defined but zero can be divided by any number except zero.

Answers: *1a)* -2, *b)* 3, *c) not defined, d)* 0; *2a)* $\dfrac{12}{5}$, *b)* 8, *c)* $-\dfrac{1}{6}$, *d)* $\dfrac{3x}{2}$; *3a)* $3 \cdot \dfrac{1}{5}$, *b)* $-\dfrac{2}{3} \cdot \left(-\dfrac{8}{5}\right)$,

c) $n \cdot p$; *4a)* $-\dfrac{4}{5}$, *b)* $\dfrac{7}{6}$, *c)* -15, *d) not defined;* *5)* -90, -4%

Properties of Real Numbers

Learning Objectives:

a   Find equivalent fraction expressions and simplify fraction expressions.
b   Use the commutative and associative laws to find equivalent expressions.
c   Use the distributive laws to multiply expressions like 8 and $x - y$.
d   Use the distributive laws to factor expressions like $4x - 12 + 24y$.
e   Collect like terms.

Examples:

1. Find an equivalent expression with the given denominator.

   a) $\dfrac{4}{7} = \dfrac{\square}{7x}$ b) $\dfrac{4}{3x} = \dfrac{\square}{6x^2}$

2. Simplify.

   a) $\dfrac{20x}{24x}$ b) $-\dfrac{15ab}{45b}$

3. Name the law (commutative, associative, or distributive) illustrated by each statement.

   a) $3 + (-7) = -7 + 3$ b) $-3 + [6 + (-2)] = (-3 + 6) + (-2)$

   c) $-5(c + d) = -5c - 5d$ d) $(-5 + 7) + 10 = 10 + (-5 + 7)$

   e) $7\left(-\dfrac{3}{7}\right) = \left(-\dfrac{3}{7}\right)7$

4. Multiply.
   a) $3(k + 6)$ b) $-5(h - 2)$ c) $-2(5a - 2b - c)$

5. Factor.
   a) $3y + 6x$ b) $12n - 3$ c) $4x - 8y + 12z$

6. Collect like terms.
   a) $8x - x$ b) $14n + 12m - 6n + 3m$
   c) $2.3x + 4.1y - 0.8x - 1.8y$

Teaching Notes:

- Remind students that the commutative laws deal with the order of addition or multiplication, whereas the associative laws deal with grouping.
- The distributive laws cover multiplication over addition and/or subtraction.
- Have students provide examples to show whether or not the commutative/associative laws hold for subtraction and division.

Answers: _1a)_ $\dfrac{4x}{7x}$, _b)_ $\dfrac{8x}{6x^2}$; _2a)_ $\dfrac{5}{6}$, _b)_ $-\dfrac{a}{3}$; _3a) commutative, b) associative, c) distributive, d) commutative,_
e) commutative; 4a) $3k + 18$, _b)_ $-5h + 10$, _c)_ $-10a + 4b + 2c$; _5a)_ $3(y + 2x)$, _b)_ $3(4n - 1)$,
_c)_ $4(x - 2y + 3z)$; _6a)_ $7x$, _b)_ $8n + 15m$, _c)_ $1.5x + 2.3y$

Simplifying Expressions; Order of Operations

Learning Objectives:

  a   Find an equivalent expression for an opposite without parentheses, where an expression has several terms.
  b   Simplify expressions by removing parentheses and collecting like terms.
  c   Simplify expressions with parentheses inside parentheses.
  d   Simplify expressions using the rules for order of operations.

Examples:

1. Find an equivalent expression without parentheses.
   a) $-(8x+3)$ b) $-(5-y)$ c) $-(-4x+8y-3z)$

2. Remove parentheses and simplify each expression.
   a) $-2(3m+6)+4m$ b) $7c-(5c+8)$ c) $3(f-4e)-2(5f-1)$

3. Simplify.
   a) $\left[4(2x+3)-5\right]-\left[3(x+2)+1\right]$ b) $5\left[12-6(7-3)\right]$

   c) $2\left\{\left[3(x-1)+2\right]-5\left[4(x+2)-6\right]\right\}$

4. Simplify.
   a) $12-2\cdot3+4$ b) $2^5\div2^3+1$ c) $14-(3-4)$

   d) $64\div2^2+4$ e) $(12-2)\cdot3+4$ f) $\dfrac{4^2+6^2}{\left|2^3-18\right|}$

Teaching Notes:

- Students have difficulty distinguishing between *terms* and *factors* – terms are separated by addition (keeping in mind that all subtractions can be written as addition of the opposite); factors are multiplied.
- Remind students that expressions can be simplified, whereas equations are solved.

Answers: *1a)* $-8x-3$, *b)* $-5+y$, *c)* $4x-8y+3z$;   *2a)* $-2m-12$, *b)* $2c-8$, *c)* $-7f-12e+2$;   *3a)* $5x$, *b)* -60, *c)* $-34x-22$;   *4a)* 10, *b)* 5, *c)* 15, *d)* 20, *e)* 34, *f)* $\dfrac{26}{5}$

Solving Equations: The Addition Principle

Learning Objectives:

    a   Determine whether a given number is a solution of a given equation.
    b   Solve equations using the addition principle.

Examples:

1. Determine whether the given number is a solution of the given equation.
    a) Is 0 a solution of $6-3x=6-5x$?
    b) Is 5 a solution of $x+4=10$?
    c) Is 9 a solution of $12=3+x$?
    d) Is 10 a solution of $8(y-3)=54$?

2. Solve using the addition principle.
    a) $x-4=16$ b) $14=x-12$ c) $x+15=18$

    d) $-19=x+16$ e) $21=-16+x$ f) $x-(-6)=18$

    g) $15=x-5$ h) $13+x=13$ i) $-26+x=-32$

3. Solve using the addition principle.
    a) $\dfrac{1}{4}+x=\dfrac{3}{4}$ b) $\dfrac{1}{3}+x=\dfrac{5}{6}$ c) $x-\dfrac{1}{5}=0$

    d) $x-\dfrac{9}{10}=-\dfrac{3}{5}$ e) $-2.2+x=16$ f) $14\dfrac{3}{4}=-28+x$

Teaching Notes:

- Encourage students to write all of the addition principle steps and to avoid using shortcuts until they have mastered these types of equations.
- Encourage students to write the steps for solving the equations in a neat and organized manner. This habit will help immensely when the equations become more complex.
- Refer students to the addition principle for equations in the text.

Answers: *1a) yes, b) no, c) yes, d) no; 2a) 20, b) 26, c) 3, d) -35, e) 37, f) 12, g) 20, h) 0, i) -6 ; 3a) $\dfrac{1}{2}$,*

b) $\dfrac{1}{2}$, c) $\dfrac{1}{5}$, d) $\dfrac{3}{10}$, e) 18.2, f) $42\dfrac{3}{4}$

Solving Equations: The Multiplication Principle

Learning Objective:

   a   Solve equations using the multiplication principle.

Examples:

1. By what number is it necessary to multiply each side of each equation in order to obtain x on the left side? Do not solve.

   a) $\frac{1}{5}x = 3$ b) $\frac{x}{6} = -2$ c) $-\frac{3}{4}x = 21$ d) $-x = 41$

2. Tell whether you would use the addition or multiplication principle to solve each equation. Do not solve.
   a) $x + 3 = -15$ b) $5x = -25$

3. Solve using the multiplication principle. Be sure to simplify your answers. Check your answers.

   a) $\frac{1}{5}x = 6$ b) $\frac{1}{4}x = -25$ c) $\frac{x}{12} = 5$ d) $-9 = \frac{x}{9}$

4. Solve using the multiplication principle. Be sure to simplify your answers. Check your answers.
   a) $3x = 9$ b) $7x = -56$ c) $-11 = 2x$ d) $1.2x = 88$

   e) $-16 = -x$ f) $-x = 100$ g) $-3.3x = -111$ h) $53 = -8x$

5. Solve using the multiplication principle. Check your answers.

   a) $\frac{1}{6}x = -9$ b) $-43 = 4x$ c) $-9.8x = -210.994$

   d) $-99 = -x$ e) $-8 = \frac{x}{8}$ f) $\frac{x}{15} = 225$

Teaching Notes:

- Some students need to be shown that $\frac{1}{12}x = \frac{1}{12} \cdot \frac{x}{1} = \frac{1 \cdot x}{12 \cdot 1} = \frac{x}{12}$.
- Refer to the multiplication principle for equations in the text.

Answers: *1a) 5, b) 6, c)* $-\frac{4}{3}$*, d)* -1*; 2a) addition principle, b) multiplication principle; 3a) 30, b)* -100*,*

c) 60, d) -81*; 4a) 3, b)* -8*, c)* $-\frac{11}{2}$ *or* $-5\frac{1}{2}$*, d)* $73.\overline{3}$ *or* $\frac{220}{3}$*, e) 16, f)* -100*, g)* $33.\overline{63}$ *or* $\frac{370}{11}$*,*

h) -6.625 *or* $-\frac{53}{8}$*; 5a)* -54*, b)* -10.75 *or* $-\frac{43}{4}$*, c) 21.53, d) 99, e)* -64*, f) 3375*

Using the Principles Together

Learning Objectives:

    a   Solve equations using both the addition principle and the multiplication principle.
    b   Solve equations in which like terms may need to be collected.
    c   Solve equations by first removing parentheses and collecting like terms; solve equations with an infinite number of solutions and equations with no solutions.

Examples:

1. Determine whether the given solution is correct.
    a) Is 12 a solution for $5x + 4 - 2x = 3x - 5 + x$?
    b) Is 9 a solution for $5x + 4 - 2x = 3x - 5 + x$?

2. Solve for x. Check your solution.
    a) $10x + 7 = 107$ b) $7x - 8 = 27$ c) $33 = 6x - 3$

    d) $164 = 15x + 14$ e) $\frac{1}{2}x - 8 = -2$ f) $-\frac{2}{3}x - 8 = -32$

3. Solve the equation. Check your solution.
    a) $4x = -2x + 60$ b) $8x - 6 = 3 + 9x$ c) $-\frac{3}{4}x - \frac{5}{2} = -\frac{5}{8} + 2x$

    d) $0.6y - 0.3 = 0.7 - 0.3y$ e) $x - 12 = 10 - x$ f) $-9x + 4 + 7x = -3x + 9$

4. Solve the equation. Check your solution.
    a) $6(2x - 1) = 30$ b) $-1(x + 11) = 20$ c) $6(x - 8) = 6x - 48$

    d) $3x + 6(x + 9) = 9x - 15$ e) $0.4x - 0.2(3 - x) = 7.6$ f) $7x - 3(x - 8) = 3x + 24$

Teaching Notes:

- Encourage students to check their solutions, as in example 1.
- In example 3, some students prefer to work to always have the variable on the left, while others prefer to work to always have a positive coefficient in front of the variable.
- Some students confuse the principles and try to subtract the coefficient from the variable instead of multiplying to obtain a coefficient of 1.
- Some students neglect to collect the like terms before trying to solve as in example 3f.

Answers: *1a) no, b) yes; 2a) 10, b) 5, c) 6, d) 10, e) 12, f) 36; 3a) 10, b) -9, c) $-\frac{15}{22}$, d) $\frac{10}{9}$ or $1\frac{1}{9}$, e) 11,*

f) 5; 4a) 3, b) -31, c) all real numbers, d) no solution, e) $\frac{41}{3}$ or $13\frac{2}{3}$, f) 0

Formulas

Learning Objectives:

    a   Evaluate a formula.
    b   Solve a formula for a specified letter.

Examples:

1.   Substitute values into the given formula and solve.
    a) The formula for the perimeter of a rectangle is $P = 2L + 2W$. If the length, L, is 9 m and the width, W, is 5 m, find the perimeter, P, of the rectangle.

    b) The area of a triangle is given by $A = \dfrac{1}{2}bh$. If the base, b, is 19 in. and the height, h, is 17 in., find the area, A, of the triangle.

2.   Solve for the indicated letter.

    a) $d = rt$, for r b) $V = \dfrac{1}{3}Bh$, for h c) $P = 2L + 2W$, for W

    d) $F = \dfrac{9}{5}C + 32$, for C e) $y = 3x + 6$, for x f) $S = 2\pi rh + 2\pi r^2$, for h

Teaching Notes:

- Many students have difficulty with the problems in example 2.
- Sometimes it is required for students to solve a number of problems using the same formula. It may be advantageous for students to rewrite the formula so that it is solved for the required letter first.
- Encourage students to label answers with the correct units.

Answers: 1a) $P = 28$ m, b) $A = 161.5$ in^2 ; 2a) $r = \dfrac{d}{t}$, b) $h = \dfrac{3V}{B}$, c) $W = \dfrac{P - 2L}{2}$, d) $C = \dfrac{5}{9}(F - 32)$,

e) $x = \dfrac{y - 6}{3}$, f) $h = \dfrac{S - 2\pi r^2}{2\pi r}$

Applications of Percent

Learning Objective:

    a   Solve applied problems involving percent.

Examples:

1. Solve.
    a) 7 is 10% of what number?   b) What is 32% of 224?   c) Find 190% of 375.

    d) 25 is what percent of 125?   e) What percent of 80 is 0.8?   f) 126 is 450% of what number?

2. Solve.
    a) The Smith family paid 22% of the purchase price of a $231,000 home as a down payment. Determine the amount of the down payment.

    b) A waiter received a tip of $7.65 on a meal which cost $42.50. What percent of the cost of the meal was the tip?

    c) Josh controlled 12 cities in a game. This was 75% of all the cities in the game. How many cities were in the game?

    d) The population of Grovestown was 2250 last year. This year it is 2295. What is the percent of increase?

Teaching Notes:

- Many students find this section difficult.
- One way to remember which way to move the decimal point when converting between decimal and percent notation is to remember that the decimal is moved right for **D**ecimal to **P**ercent, and left for **P**ercent to **D**ecimal.

Answers: *1a) 70, b) 71.68, c) 712.5, d) 20%, e) 1%, f) 28; 2a) $50,820, b) 18%, c) 16 cities, d) 2%*

Applications and Problem Solving

Learning Objective:

    a   Solve applied problems by translating to equations.

Examples:

1. Solve.
    a) If 5 is added to a number, and the sum is tripled, the result is 11 more than the number. Find the number.

    b) When six is subtracted from half of a number, the result is -18. What is the original number?

2. In 2008, Pierre's Pizza and Burger Palace together had revenue totaling $470,000. If Burger Palace took in $90,000 less than Pierre's Pizza, how much did each take in as revenue?

3. The perimeter of a triangle is 37 ft. One side of the triangle is 2 ft longer than the second side. The third side is 5 ft longer than the second side. Find the length of each side.

4. Solve.
    a) The sum of two consecutive integers is 59. Find the integers.

    b) When the lesser of two consecutive odd integers is added to twice the greater, the result is 187. Find the integers.

5. A parking lot charges $2.50 for the first hour or part thereof, and $1.25 for each additional hour or part thereof. For how many hours did Gwen park if her total fee was $10?

Teaching Notes:

- Many students find these problems difficult at first.
- Refer students to the five-step problem-solving strategy in the text.
- Encourage students to check whether their final answers are reasonable.

Answers: 1a) -2, b) -24 ; 2) Pierre's Pizza had revenue of $280,000 and Burger Palace had revenue of $190,000; 3) 12 ft, 10 ft, 15 ft; 4a) 29 and 30, b) 61 and 63; 5) 7 hr

Solving Inequalities

Learning Objectives:

a   Determine whether a given number is a solution of an inequality.
b   Graph an inequality on the number line.
c   Solve inequalities using the addition principle.
d   Solve inequalities using the multiplication principle.
e   Solve inequalities using the addition principle and the multiplication principle together.

Examples:

1. Determine whether each number is a solution of $x \leq -4$.
   a) -2 b) -5 c) 3 d) -4

2. Graph each inequality on the number line.

   a) $x > 1$ b) $x \geq -4$ c) $x < \dfrac{2}{3}$ d) $x \leq -2.5$ e) $-3 \leq x < 1$

3. Translate each graph to an inequality using the variable x.

  a) 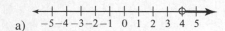   b)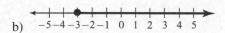

  c) 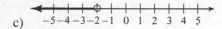   d)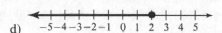

4. Solve each inequality.

   a) $x + 3 < -5$ b) $x - \dfrac{1}{3} > -\dfrac{2}{9}$ c) $4x \geq -32$ d) $-6x \leq 18$

   e) $4x - 10 > 5x + 4$ f) $5x - 2 \leq 6x + 4$ g) $-4x - 7 < 5(2x + 7)$ h) $7(x - 3) > 2(5x - 8)$

Teaching Notes:

- Some students are unfamiliar with $<$, $>$, $\leq$, and $\geq$ and need to be taught the definitions of each.
- Some students need extra help with examples 2c and 2d.

Answers: *1a) no, b) yes, c) no, d) yes; 2a-e) see graph answer pages; 3a)* $\{x | x > 4\}$, *b)* $\{x | x \geq -3\}$,

c) $\{x | x < -2\}$, *d)* $\{x | x \leq 2\}$; *4a)* $\{x | x < -8\}$, *b)* $\left\{x \middle| x > \dfrac{1}{9}\right\}$, *c)* $\{x | x \geq -8\}$, *d)* $\{x | x \geq -3\}$,

e) $\{x | x < -14\}$, *f)* $\{x | x \geq -6\}$, *g)* $\{x | x > -3\}$, *h)* $\left\{x \middle| x < -\dfrac{5}{3}\right\}$

Applications and Problem Solving with Inequalities

Learning Objectives:

    a   Translate number sentences to inequalities.
    b   Solve applied problems using inequalities.

Examples:

1. Translate to an inequality.
    a) A number is greater than -3.

    b) The capacity was at least 200.

    c) Six more than a number is less than 21.

    d) The cost is no more than $500.

2. Solve using an inequality.
    a) A certain car has a weight limit for all passengers and cargo of 1129 lb. The four passengers in the car weigh an average of 165 lb. Find the weight of the cargo that the car can handle.

    b) A certain store has a fax machine available for use by its customers. The store charges $1.85 to send the first page and $0.45 for each subsequent page. Find the number of pages that can be faxed for $7.25.

    c) An archery set containing a bow and three arrows costs $68. Additional arrows can be purchased for $9 each. Jerry has $230 to spend on the set and additional arrows. Including the arrows in the set, how many arrows can Jerry purchase?

Teaching Notes:

- Review the common English-to-inequality translations.
- Some students benefit from seeing solutions on the number line.

Answers: *1a)* $n > -3$, *b)* $c \geq 200$, *c)* $6 + n < 21$, *d)* $c \leq 500$; *2a)* $\{x | x \leq 469 \ lb\}$, *b)* $\{x | x \leq 13 \ pages\}$, *c)* $\{x | x \leq 21 \ arrows\}$

Graphs and Applications of Linear Equations

Learning Objectives:

    a   Plot points associated with ordered pairs of numbers; determine the quadrant in which a point lies.
    b   Find the coordinates of a point on a graph.
    c   Determine whether an ordered pair is a solution of an equation with two variables.
    d   Graph linear equations of the type $y = mx + b$ and $Ax + By = C$, identifying the y-intercept.
    e   Solve applied problems involving graphs of linear equations.

Examples:

1.   Identify and label the following features on the rectangular coordinate system.
      a) x-axis   b) y-axis   c) x-values –6 to 6
      d) y-values –6 to 6   e) origin (0, 0)   f) ordered pair (3, 4)
      g) ordered pair (–2, –5)

2.   Determine whether each ordered pair is a solution of the equation $3x - y = 5$.
      a) $(0, -5)$ b) $(2, -1)$ c) $(-1, -8)$

3. Complete the ordered-pair solutions. Then plot each solution and graph the equation by connecting the points by a straight line.
      a) $y = x - 3$ b) $y = -3x + 2$ c) $4x + 3y = 0$
        (7,) (–2,) (0,)   (0,) (1,) (–1,)   (–3,) (0,) (3,)

4.   Graph each equation and identify the y-intercept.
      a) $y = 3x + 4$ b) $2x + 3y = 6$ c) $y = -\dfrac{1}{2}x + 4$ d) $\dfrac{2}{5}x + y = 3$

5. The population of an endangered species of fish living in a controlled habitat is given by the equation $P = 7t + 46$, where P is the population and t is the time in months since the population was moved to the habitat.
    a) Graph the equation using $t = 0, 6, 12,$ and 18.
    b) In what month will the number of fish be about 110?

Teaching Notes:

- Some students are unfamiliar with graphing and need to see the number line graph first, and then a perpendicular y-axis added to it to make a rectangular coordinate system.
- Some students are very confused by the fact that they can choose any value of x or y as a starting point for finding an ordered-pair solution.
- Many students have trouble creating the correct graphing scale on applied problems.

Answers: *1a-g) see graph answer pages; 2a) yes, b) no, c) yes; 3a) 4, –5, –3, see graph answer pages,*
b) 2, –1, 5, see graph answer pages, c) 4, 0, –4, see graph answer pages; 4a-d) see graph answer pages;
5a) see graph answer pages, b) month 9

More with Graphing and Intercepts

Learning Objectives:

    a   Find the intercepts of a linear equation, and graph using intercepts.
    b   Graph equations equivalent to those of the type $x = a$ and $y = b$.

Examples:

1. Find the coordinates of (i) the y-intercept and (ii) the x-intercept.
    a) $4x - 3y = 12$ b) $6x + 5y = -30$ c) $5x - 10 = 3y$ d) $8y - 3 = 6x$

2. Graph each equation by plotting the intercepts and one other point.
    a) $y = 3x + 4$ b) $2x + 3y = 6$ c) $y = -\dfrac{1}{2}x + 4$ d) $\dfrac{2}{5}x + y = 3$

3. Graph the equation. Be sure to simplify the equation before graphing it.
    a) $x = 4$ b) $y = -3$ c) $2x + 6 = 5x$ d) $y - 4 = 3y$

Teaching Notes:

- Many students do not understand the equations in problem 3 and must memorize which case gives a horizontal line and which case gives a vertical line.
- Students sometimes mix-up the x- and y-intercepts.

Answers: 1a) (i) $(0, -4)$, (ii) $(3, 0)$, b) (i) $(0, -6)$, (ii) $(-5, 0)$, c) (i) $\left(0, -\dfrac{10}{3}\right)$, (ii) $(2, 0)$, d) (i) $\left(0, \dfrac{3}{8}\right)$,

(ii) $\left(-\dfrac{1}{2}, 0\right)$; 2-3) see graph answer pages

Slope and Applications

Learning Objectives:

a   Given the coordinates of two points on a line, find the slope of the line, if it exists.
b   Find the slope of a line from an equation.
c   Find the slope, or rate of change, in an applied problem involving slope.

Examples:

1. Find the slope, if it exists, of a line containing the given pair of points.
    a) (5, 3) and (9, 6)   b) (–5, 8) and (–3, –9)   c) (–8, –5) and (–3, –5)

    d) (–8, 5) and (–8, 4)   e) (–3, –4) and (6, –4)   f) (–3, 3) and (0, 0)

2. Find the slope, if it exists, of each line.
    a) $y = -2x$ b) $y = \dfrac{2}{3}x + 4$ c) $-3x + 4y = -12$

    d) $x = -5$ e) $x = -\dfrac{1}{5}y + 6$ f) $y = 6$

3. From a base elevation of 1700 ft, Jackson's Peak rises to a summit elevation of 3200 ft over a horizontal distance of 9700 ft. Find the grade of Jackson's Peak.

Teaching Notes:

*   Most students need to hear a qualitative description of slope before using the slope formula in problem 1. For example, show sketches of lines with +, –, 0, and undefined slope and discuss what happens to y as x increases. Then the slope formula gives a quantitative measure of the change in y as x increases.
*   Many students make sign errors when calculating the slopes in problem 1.

Answers: _1a) 3/4, b) –17/2, c) 0, d) not defined, e) 0, f) –1; 2a) –2, b)_ $\dfrac{2}{3}$, _c)_ $\dfrac{3}{4}$, _d) not defined, e) –5, f) 0;_
_3) 15.5%_

Equations of Lines

Learning Objectives:

a   Given an equation in the form $y = mx + b$, find the slope and the y-intercept; find an equation of a line when the slope and the y-intercept are given.

b   Find an equation of a line when the slope and a point on the line are given.

c   Find an equation of a line when two points on the line are given.

Examples:

1. Find the slope and the y–intercept.

   a) $y = 3x + 4$ b) $y = -2x + 9$ c) $y = \dfrac{4}{3}x - \dfrac{3}{5}$

   d) $2x + 5y = 3$ e) $y = -3$ f) $y = 1.2x$

2. Write the equation of the line with the given slope and y-intercept.

   a) slope = 2, y–intercept = $(0, -4)$ b) slope = $-\dfrac{3}{2}$, y–intercept = $\left(0, \dfrac{5}{6}\right)$

3. Find an equation of the line that has the given slope and contains the given point.

   a) $m = 3,\ (0, 4)$ b) $m = 2,\ (4, -4)$

   c) $m = -3,\ \left(\dfrac{3}{2}, 2\right)$ d) $m = \dfrac{2}{3},\ (4, -2)$

4. Write an equation of the line that contains the given points.

   a) $(2, 14)$ and $(-4, -4)$ b) $(1, -16)$ and $(-2, -1)$ c) $\left(2, \dfrac{4}{3}\right)$ and $\left(\dfrac{2}{3}, \dfrac{2}{3}\right)$

5. Let the ordered pairs $(3, 125)$ and $(8, 220)$ represent the number of fish caught in a lake where 3 represents March and 8 represents August, and 125 and 220 represent the numbers of fish caught.
   a) Use these ordered pairs to write an equation of the line that contains them.
   b) What is the rate of change of fish caught with respect to time during this period?
   c) Use the equation to estimate the number of fish caught in June.

Teaching Notes:

*   In problems 3 and 4, many students are confused by having to find the value of b, and are not sure what to do with it once they find it.
*   Some students do not understand leaving x and y as variables in the final equation.

Answers: *1a) slope 3, y-int (0, 4), b) slope –2, y-int (0, 9), c) slope 4/3, y-int (0, –3/5), d) slope –2/5,*

y-int (0, 3/5), e) slope 0, y-int $(0, -3)$, f) slope 1.2, y-int (0,0); 2a) $y = 2x - 4$, b) $y = -\dfrac{3}{2}x + \dfrac{5}{6}$;

3a) $y = 3x + 4$, b) $y = 2x - 12$, c) $y = -3x + \dfrac{13}{2}$, d) $y = \dfrac{2}{3}x - \dfrac{14}{3}$; 4a) $y = 3x + 8$, b) $y = -5x - 11$,

c) $y = \dfrac{1}{2}x + \dfrac{1}{3}$; 5a) $y = 19x + 68$, b) 19 fish/mo, c) 182 fish

Graphing Using the Slope and the *y*-Intercept

Learning Objective:

    a   Use the slope and the *y*-intercept to graph a line.

Examples:

1. Determine the slope and the *y*-intercept of each line.

    a) $y = \dfrac{2}{3}x - 4$ b) $y = -\dfrac{5}{4}x + 2$ c) $y - 3x = -4$ d) $y = 2x$

2. Graph the lines in example 1 using the slopes and the *y*-intercepts.

Teaching Note:

- Many students find graphing using the slope and *y*-intercept difficult at first. Remind them to check if their final line has the correct slope sign.

Answers: *1a) slope 2/3, y-intercept (0, –4), b) slope –5/4, y-intercept (0, 2), c) slope 3, y-intercept (0, –4),*
d) slope 2, y-intercept (0, 0); 2) see graph answer pages

Parallel and Perpendicular Lines

Learning Objectives:

    a   Determine whether the graphs of two linear equations are parallel.
    b   Determine whether the graphs of two linear equations are perpendicular.

Examples:

1. Determine whether the graphs of the equations are parallel lines.
    a) $4x - 2 = y$,   b) $y = 3x + 6$,   c) $y = -5$,
       $y - 4x = 6$ $2y + 6x = 8$ $y = x - 4$

2. Determine whether the graphs of the equations are perpendicular lines.
    a) $y = 3$,   b) $5x - 3 = y$,   c) $3x - 4y = 12$,
       $x = -2$ $5y + x = 6$ $4x - 3y = 8$

3. Determine whether the graphs of the equations are parallel, perpendicular, or neither.
    a) $x - y = 5$,   b) $2x - 3y = 6$,   c) $-x + 4y = 5$,
       $x + y = -2$ $6y + 5 = -4x$ $7 + 2x = 8y$

Teaching Notes:

- A common mistake is for students to consider lines to be perpendicular if their slopes are opposites of each other or are reciprocals of each other.
- Remind students that two vertical lines are parallel to each other and that a horizontal line and a vertical line are perpendicular to each other.

Answers: *1a) yes, b) no, c) no; 2a) yes, b) yes, c) no; 3a) perpendicular, b) neither, c) parallel*

Graphing Inequalities in Two Variables

Learning Objectives:

    a   Determine whether an ordered pair of numbers is a solution of an inequality in two variables.
    b   Graph linear inequalities.

Examples:

1. Determine whether the ordered pair is a solution of $y \geq x + 2$.

    a)   (0, 2)   b)   (1, 4)   c)   (−1, −2)

2. Graph on a plane.

    a) $y < x$ b) $y \geq x + 2$ c) $y \leq -x - 3$

    d) $y > -5x + 3$ e) $x + 2y > -2$ f) $-2x - 5y \leq 10$

    g) $y > \frac{1}{2}x$ h) $y \leq 2$ i) $x \geq -2$

    j) $2x < -3y$ k) $x > -3y$ l) $2x \leq 3 + y$

Teaching Notes:

- Most students who are good at graphing linear equations find this section easy.
- Although students do not fully understand the region they are testing in problem 1 until they graph it in 2b), many of them need to practice testing ordered pairs before they use this skill within a graphing problem.
- Remind students to always use a test point from the graphed region to check their work.
- Remind students to use a dashed line for < or > and a solid line for ≤ or ≥ inequalities.
- Refer students to the **Graphing Linear Inequalities** steps in the textbook.

Answers: *1a) yes, b) yes, c) no; 2a–l) see graph answer pages*

Integers as Exponents

Learning Objectives:

    a   Tell the meaning of exponential notation.
    b   Evaluate exponential expressions with exponents of 0 and 1.
    c   Evaluate algebraic expressions containing exponents.
    d   Use the product rule to multiply exponential expressions with like bases.
    e   Use the quotient rule to divide exponential expressions with like bases.
    f   Express an exponential expression involving negative exponents with positive exponents.

Examples:

1. What is the meaning of each of the following?

    a) 8^3 b) $(11x)^4$ c) $-7x^5$

2. Evaluate each expression.

    a) $y^0, y \neq 0$ b) $(-4.2)^1$ c) $(-11)^0$ d) $\dfrac{0^5}{5^0}$ e) m^1

3. Evaluate.
    a) x^4, when $x = 2$ b) $y^3 - 8$, when $y = 4$ c) $k^0 + 2$, when $k = 8$

4. Express using positive exponents. Then simplify.

    a) x^{-3} b) $2x^{-3}$ c) $\dfrac{1}{a^{-7}}$ d) $\dfrac{2}{3y^{-2}}$

5. Multiply. Leave your answer in exponential notation using positive exponents.
    a) $4^2 \cdot 4^3$ b) $x^8 \cdot x^6$ c) $(2p^4)(6p^5)$ d) $(-3y)(5y^7)(2y^3)$

    e) $(7x^4y^3)(3xy^6)$ f) $\left(\dfrac{2}{3}m^4n^3\right)\left(-\dfrac{3}{4}mn^6\right)$ g) $(2.3abc)(8.8a^2b^5)$ h) $x^{-3} \cdot x^{-5}$

6. Divide. Leave your answer in exponential notation using positive exponents.
    a) $\dfrac{6^5}{6^3}$ b) $\dfrac{x^7}{x^4}$ c) $\dfrac{y^3}{y^8}$ d) $\dfrac{6x^9}{2x^8}$

    e) $\dfrac{-12x^8y^3}{6x^{10}y}$ f) $\dfrac{24a^4b}{36a^4b^3}$ g) $\dfrac{-30x^0yz^3}{15yz^2}$ h) $\dfrac{a^{-3}}{a^{-2}}$

Teaching Notes:

- Students need <u>a lot</u> of repetition and practice in order to master these objectives.
- Students often move constants along with a variable that has a negative exponent. For example, in 4b) a common incorrect answer is $2x^{-3} = 1/(2x^3)$.

Answers: 1a) $8 \cdot 8 \cdot 8$, b) $(11x)(11x)(11x)(11x)$, c) $-7 \cdot x \cdot x \cdot x \cdot x \cdot x$; 2a) 1, b) -4.2, c) 1, d) 0, e) m; 3a) 16,

b) 56, c) 3; 4a) $\dfrac{1}{x^3}$, b) $\dfrac{2}{x^3}$, c) a^7, d) $\dfrac{2y^2}{3}$; 5a) 4^5, b) x^{14}, c) $12p^9$, d) $-30y^{11}$, e) $21x^5y^9$, f) $-\dfrac{1}{2}m^5n^9$,

g) $20.24a^3b^6c$, h) $\dfrac{1}{x^8}$; 6a) 6^2, b) x^3, c) $\dfrac{1}{y^5}$, d) $3x$, e) $\dfrac{-2y^2}{x^2}$, f) $\dfrac{2}{3b^2}$, g) $-2z$, h) $\dfrac{1}{a}$

Exponents and Scientific Notation

Learning Objectives:

    a   Use the power rule to raise powers to powers.
    b   Raise a product to a power and a quotient to a power.
    c   Convert between scientific notation and decimal notation.
    d   Multiply and divide using scientific notation.
    e   Solve applied problems using scientific notation.

Examples:

1. Simplify.

    a) $(x^2)^3$
    b) $(a^2b^3)^4$
    c) $(2xy^3)^5$
    d) $\left(\dfrac{-6x}{y^3}\right)^3$

    e) $\left(\dfrac{a^2b^3}{c^5d}\right)^4$
    f) $\left(\dfrac{3x^3y^0}{z^2}\right)^{-3}$
    g) $\left(x^{-3}y^{-4}\right)^5$
    h) $\left(-2a^{-4}b\right)^{-3}$

2. Convert to scientific notation.
    a) 125
    b) 3442
    c) 0.022
    d) 0.00000453

3. Convert to standard notation.
    a) 2.04×10^3
    b) 1.9902×10^7
    c) 9.311×10^{-4}
    d) 10^{-5}

4. Multiply or divide and write scientific notation for the result.
    a) $\left(7\times10^{-3}\right)\left(5\times10^{-9}\right)$
    b) $\left(9\times10^6\right)\left(4\times10^7\right)$

    c) $\dfrac{8\times10^{-3}}{2\times10^{-4}}$
    d) $\dfrac{9.18\times10^1}{6.8\times10^3}$

5. The Amazon River discharges approximately 250 million cubic feet of water per minute. How much water is discharged in a week? Express the answer in scientific notation.

Teaching Notes:

- Students need a lot of repetition and practice in order to master these objectives.
- Remind students that exactly one digit must precede the decimal point when writing a number in scientific notation (e.g., $d.ddd...\times10^n$).

Answers: 1a) x^6, b) a^8b^{12}, c) $32x^5y^{15}$, d) $\dfrac{-216x^3}{y^9}$, e) $\dfrac{a^8b^{12}}{c^{20}d^4}$, f) $\dfrac{z^6}{27x^9}$, g) $\dfrac{1}{x^{15}y^{20}}$, h) $-\dfrac{a^{12}}{8b^3}$;

2a) 1.25×10^2, b) 3.442×10^3, c) 2.2×10^{-2}, d) 4.53×10^{-6} ; 3a) 2040, b) 19,902,000, c) 0.0009311, d) 0.00001, 4a) 3.5×10^{-11}, b) 3.6×10^{14}, c) 4×10^1, d) 1.35×10^{-2} ; 5) 2.52×10^{12} ft^3

Introduction to Polynomials

Learning Objectives:

    a   Evaluate a polynomial for a given value of the variable.
    b   Identify the terms of a polynomial.
    c   Identify the like terms of a polynomial.
    d   Identify the coefficients of a polynomial.
    e   Collect the like terms of a polynomial.
    f   Arrange a polynomial in descending order, or collect the like terms and then arrange in descending order.
    g   Identify the degree of each term of a polynomial and the degree of the polynomial.
    h   Identify the missing terms of a polynomial.
    i   Classify a polynomial as a monomial, a binomial, a trinomial, or none of these.

Examples:

1. Evaluate $x^3 - 4x^2 + x + 1$ for $x = -2$.

2. For the polynomial $-4x^5 + 6x^2 + x - 6$,
   a) Identify the terms.
   b) Identify the coefficient of each term.
   c) Identify the degree of each term.

3. State the degree of the polynomial and whether it is a monomial, binomial, or trinomial.
   a) $2y^7$ b) $12x^5 - 3x^2 + 2$ c) $9x^3 + 10x^4$

4. Collect like terms and arrange in descending order.
   a) $12y - 8y$ b) $7x^2 - 3x + 5x^2 - 9x$
   c) $-x + 21x^3 - 6x^2 + 4x + 2x^2$ d) $8y^3 + 6y^4 - y^3 + y - 2y^4$
   e) $4 + 8z + 5z^2 - z^2 + 12$ f) $x^2 + 8x^2 - 10x^3 - 5x^2 + x^3$

5. Identify the missing terms in each polynomial.
   a) $x^3 + 8$ b) $4x^4 - 2x^2 + 6$

Teaching Notes:

- Some students have difficulty identifying a coefficient of 1 or -1.
- Some students have difficulty understanding a degree of 0 or 1.
- Some students like to set up problems vertically, aligning the like terms.

Answers: *1) -25; 2a) $-4x^5, 6x^2, x, -6$, b) $-4, 6, 1, -6$, c) $5, 2, 1, 0$; 3a) 7, monomial, b) 5, trinomial, c) 4, binomial; 4a) $4y$, b) $12x^2 - 12x$, c) $21x^3 - 4x^2 + 3x$, d) $4y^4 + 7y^3 + y$, e) $4z^2 + 8z + 16$, f) $-9x^3 + 4x^2$; 5a) x^2, x, b) x^3, x*

Addition and Subtraction of Polynomials

Learning Objectives:

    a   Add polynomials.
    b   Simplify the opposite of a polynomial.
    c   Subtract polynomials.
    d   Use polynomials to represent perimeter and area.

Examples:

1. Add.

    a) $(2x - 12) + (-3x + 22)$ b) $(5x^2 - 3x - 6) + (2x^2 - 8x - 3)$

    c) $\left(\dfrac{3}{4}x^2 - \dfrac{1}{3}x - 12\right) + \left(-\dfrac{1}{3}x^2 + \dfrac{2}{9}x + 3\right)$ d) $(-2.2x^3 + 5.4x - 0.1) + (6.4x - 3.4)$

2. Simplify.
    a) $-\left(-4x^2\right)$ b) $-\left(x^2 + 6x\right)$ c) $-\left(8x^3 - 2x + 1\right)$

3. Subtract.

    a) $(4x - 8) - (3x - 4)$ b) $(6x^3 + 5x^2 - 3) - (-2x^3 + 3x^2 - x + 1)$

    c) $\left(\dfrac{5}{8}x^2 - \dfrac{1}{3}x - 7\right) - \left(\dfrac{2}{3}x^2 - \dfrac{3}{4}x + 5\right)$ d) $(2.3x^4 - 4x^3 + 5x) - (x^4 - 6.2x^2 + 2.2x)$

4. Find a polynomial for the perimeter of a rectangle with length $5x$ and width 4.

Teaching Notes:

- Most students find this section easy.
- Remind students that this section is a review of distributing and collecting like terms.
- Some students like to set up the problems, vertically aligning the like terms.
- Some students forget to subtract every term when aligning vertically.

Answers: *1a)* $-x + 10$, *b)* $7x^2 - 11x - 9$, *c)* $(5/12)x^2 - (1/9)x - 9$, *d)* $-2.2x^3 + 11.8x - 3.5$; *2a)* $4x^2$,
b) $-x^2 - 6x$, *c)* $-8x^3 + 2x - 1$; *3a)* $x - 4$, *b)* $8x^3 + 2x^2 + x - 4$, *c)* $(-1/24)x^2 + (5/12)x - 12$,
d) $1.3x^4 - 4x^3 + 6.2x^2 + 2.8x$; *4)* $10x + 8$

Multiplication of Polynomials

Learning Objectives:

    a   Multiply monomials.
    b   Multiply a monomial and any polynomial.
    c   Multiply two binomials.
    d   Multiply any two polynomials.

Examples:

1. Multiply.

    a) $(5x^3)(4)$ b) $(-x^4)(x^5)$ c) $\left(\frac{1}{2}x\right)(16x^8)$

2. Multiply.
    a) $2x^2(6x-3)$ b) $4x(-2x^4+6x)$ c) $5x^3(-2x^3+7x-1)$

    d) $\frac{2}{3}(5x+6x^2-7x^3)$ e) $(3x^3+x^2-5x)(3x)$ f) $(2x^2-4x+8)(-3x)$

3. Multiply.
    a) $(x+2)(x+3)$ b) $(x+2)(x-6)$ c) $(x-4)(x-5)$

    d) $(3x-2)(-5x-6)$ e) $(4x-3)(3x-4)$ f) $(6x-3)(6x-3)$

    g) $(4-3z)(5-7z)$ h) $(0.5x+2)(6x-0.2)$ i) $\left(\frac{1}{2}x-\frac{1}{3}\right)\left(\frac{1}{3}x+\frac{1}{4}\right)$

4. Find the area of the rectangle with sides $(3x-4)$ and $(5x+3)$.

5. Multiply.
    a) $(x^3+2x^2-3x+1)(x+2)$ b) $(2x-3)(2x^3-3x^2+2x-1)$

Teaching Notes:

- Most students find this section easy.
- When multiplying two polynomials, encourage students to find products in whatever order makes sense to them, as long as each term in one polynomial is multiplied by each term in the other polynomial.

Answers: *1a)* $20x^3$, *b)* $-x^9$, *c)* $8x^9$;   *2a)* $12x^3-6x^2$, *b)* $-8x^5+24x^2$, *c)* $-10x^6+35x^4-5x^3$,
d) $(-14/3)x^3+4x^2+(10/3)x$, *e)* $9x^4+3x^3-15x^2$, *f)* $-6x^3+12x^2-24x$;   *3a)* x^2+5x+6, *b)* $x^2-4x-12$,
c) $x^2-9x+20$, *d)* $-15x^2-8x+12$, *e)* $12x^2-25x+12$, *f)* $36x^2-36x+9$, *g)* $20-43z+21z^2$,
h) $3x^2+11.9x-0.4$, *i)* $(1/6)x^2+(1/72)x-(1/12)$;   *4)* $15x^2-11x-12$;   *5a)* $x^4+4x^3+x^2-5x+2$,
b) $4x^4-12x^3+13x^2-8x+3$

Special Products

Learning Objectives:

  a Multiply two binomials mentally using the FOIL method.
  b Multiply the sum and the difference of two terms mentally.
  c Square a binomial mentally.
  d Find special products when polynomial products are mixed together.

Examples:

1. Multiply.

  a) $(x-5)(x^2+3)$ b) $(a+4)(a+6)$ c) $(2y-3)(8y-5)$

  d) $(4x^3+1)(x-2)$ e) $(m-0.2)(m+0.2)$ f) $\left(k+\dfrac{3}{4}\right)\left(k+\dfrac{3}{4}\right)$

2. Multiply mentally, if possible.

  a) $(x+2)(x-2)$ b) $(x+7)(x-7)$ c) $(3x-5)(3x+5)$

  d) $(4x-3)(4x+3)$ e) $(6a-1)(6a+1)$ f) $(3x-0.2)(3x+0.2)$

3. Multiply mentally, if possible.

  a) $(3x-1)^2$ b) $(4x+5)^2$ c) $(7x-3)^2$

  d) $(3x+2)^2$ e) $\left(\dfrac{2}{3}x+\dfrac{1}{4}\right)^2$ f) $(3-4x)^2$

4. Multiply mentally, if possible.

  a) $\left(3-4x^2\right)^2$ b) $\left(7p^2+1\right)\left(7p^2-1\right)$

  c) $5x^2\left(-x^4+6x^2+11\right)$ d) $(m+2)\left(m^2-2m+4\right)$

Teaching Notes:

- Encourage students to memorize the formulas for multiplying a sum and a difference of two terms and also a square of a binomial. These will come in handy for factoring later.
- Some students have trouble remembering the formulas. Encourage them to think of multiplying polynomials as distributing. As long as each term in one polynomial is distributed onto each term in the other polynomial, they will get the right answer.
- Some students have trouble keeping track of all the terms when multiplying in problems like 4d. Encourage them to line up like terms vertically as they multiply.
- Many students square both terms rather than multiply the binomial by itself in problem 3.

Answers: *1a)* $x^3-5x^2+3x-15$, *b)* $a^2+10a+24$, *c)* $16y^2-34y+15$, *d)* $4x^4-8x^3+x-2$,

e) $m^2-0.04$, *f)* $k^2+\dfrac{3}{2}k+\dfrac{9}{16}$; *2a)* x^2-4, *b)* x^2-49, *c)* $9x^2-25$, *d)* $16x^2-9$, *e)* $36a^2-1$, *f)* $9x^2-0.04$;

3a) $9x^2-6x+1$, *b)* $16x^2+40x+25$, *c)* $49x^2-42x+9$, *d)* $9x^2+12x+4$, *e)* $(4/9)x^2+(1/3)x+(1/16)$,

f) $9-24x+16x^2$; *4a)* $9-24x^2+16x^4$, *b)* $49p^4-1$, *c)* $-5x^6+30x^4+55x^2$, *d)* m^3+8

Operations with Polynomials in Several Variables

Learning Objectives:

    a   Evaluate a polynomial in several variables for given values of the variables.
    b   Identify the coefficients and the degrees of the terms of a polynomial and the degree of a polynomial.
    c   Collect like terms of a polynomial.
    d   Add polynomials.
    e   Subtract polynomials.
    f   Multiply polynomials.

Examples:

1. Evaluate $5x^2y^3 + 6xy - y^2$ for $x = 10$ and $y = -2$.

2. For the polynomial in example 1,
   a) Identify the coefficients of the terms of the polynomial.
   b) Identify the degree of the terms of the polynomial.
   c) Identify the degree of the polynomial.

3. Collect like terms: $5x^2y + 4xy^2 + 5xy^2 - 6x^2y$.

4. Perform the indicated operation.
   a) $\left(7x^3 + 4x^2y + 7xy^2 - 3y^3\right) + \left(2x^3 + 5x^2y + 8xy^2\right)$

       b) $\left(6a^2b + 4ab\right) - \left(5ab + 6ab^2 - a^2b\right)$

   c) $\left(3x^3 + x^2 - 5x\right)(3xy)$

       d) $(4y - 3z)(5y - 7z)$

   e) $(3y - 4xz)^2$

       f) $(x + y + z)(x + y + z)$

Teaching Notes:

- Some students do not realize that $xy = yx$, and that they are therefore like terms.
- Some students are not careful to note that xy^2 and x^2y are not like terms.

Answers: 1) -4124; 2a) $5, 6, -1$, b) $5, 2, 2$, c) 5; 3) $-x^2y + 9xy^2$; 4a) $9x^3 + 9x^2y + 15xy^2 - 3y^3$,
b) $7a^2b - ab - 6ab^2$, c) $9x^4y + 3x^3y - 15x^2y$, d) $20y^2 - 43yz + 21z^2$, e) $9y^2 - 24xyz + 16x^2z^2$,
f) $x^2 + 2xy + 2xz + y^2 + 2yz + z^2$

Division of Polynomials

Learning Objectives:

    a   Divide a polynomial by a monomial.
    b   Divide a polynomial by a divisor that is a binomial.

Examples:

1. Divide and check.

    a) $\dfrac{32x^5}{4}$

    b) $\dfrac{-24a^2b^5c^{10}}{6ab^3c^4}$

    c) $\dfrac{16p^2 - 32p^5 + 4p^7}{4p}$

    d) $\left(25x^2y^2 + 15x^2y - 35xy^2\right) \div \left(5xy\right)$

2. Divide.

    a) $\dfrac{x^2 + 18x + 81}{x + 9}$

    b) $\dfrac{2m^2 + 11m - 40}{m + 8}$

    c) $\dfrac{6m^3 + 49m^2 - 36m + 81}{m + 9}$

3. Divide.

    a) $\dfrac{x^2 + 2x - 5}{x + 4}$

    b) $\dfrac{x^2 + 17x + 66}{x + 8}$

    c) $\dfrac{4x^2 - 22x + 32}{2x + 3}$

    d) $\dfrac{9x^2 + 6x + 10}{3x - 2}$

    e) $\dfrac{3y^4 + y^2 + 2}{y + 1}$

    f) $\dfrac{y^3 + 1}{y + 1}$

Teaching Notes:

- Some students cancel the denominator with the first term in the numerator and do not know what to do next.
- Most students find dividing by a binomial very confusing at first.
- Most students understand the steps for dividing by a binomial better if a numerical long division problem is shown in parallel.

Answers: *1a)* $8x^5$ *, b)* $-4ab^2c^6$ *, c)* $4p - 8p^4 + p^6$ *, d)* $5xy + 3x - 7y$ *; 2a)* $x + 9$ *, b)* $2m - 5$ *, c)* $6m^2 - 5m + 9$ *;*

3a) $x - 2 + \dfrac{3}{x+4}$ *, b)* $x + 9 - \dfrac{6}{x+8}$ *, c)* $2x - 14 + \dfrac{74}{2x+3}$ *, d)* $3x + 4 + \dfrac{18}{3x-2}$ *, e)* $3y^3 - 3y^2 + 4y - 4 + \dfrac{6}{y+1}$ *,*

f) $y^2 - y + 1$

Introduction to Factoring

Learning Objectives:

    a   Find the greatest common factor, the GCF, of monomials.
    b   Factor polynomials when the terms have a common factor, factoring out the greatest common factor.
    c   Factor certain expressions with four terms using factoring by grouping.

Examples:

1. Find the GCF.
    a) $5x^2, x^5$
    b) $12x^3, -15x^2$
    c) $-21a^2b^5, 14a^4b^3, 35ab^7$

2. Factor. Check by multiplying.
    a) $3x^2 + 6x$
    b) $4y^2 + 4y$
    c) $8a^2b^2 - 32ab$

    d) $15xy - 18yz - 27xz$
    e) $36a^2 - 24ab - 16a$
    f) $15x^2y - 25xy^2 + 20xy$

3. Factor.
    a) $3(2x + y) - z(2x + y)$
    b) $7x(x - 5) + 3(x - 5)$
    c) $4x(2y + 3z) - 7t(2y + 3z)$

    d) $12x^3 + 8x^2 - 15x - 10$
    e) $x + 2d + 5c^2x + 10c^2d$
    f) $5xy - 2x - 5y + 2$

    g) $pq + 3q + 5p + 15$

Teaching Notes:

- Some students need to rewrite the coefficients in problem 1 in factored form in order to identify the common factors.
- Encourage students to factor monomials in a step-by-step manner: first factor out the common number, then the common power of the variable for each variable that exists.
- Many students omit the 1 in the answer for 2b). Encourage students to check their answers by multiplying to avoid this problem.
- Most students find it difficult to factor common binomials. Remind them that they are still factoring a common factor, as in problem 1, but the factor happens to be a binomial.

Answers: 1a) x^2, b) $3x^2$, c) $7ab^3$; 2a) $3x(x + 2)$, b) $4y(y + 1)$, c) $8ab(ab - 4)$, d) $3(5xy - 6yz - 9xz)$, e) $4a(9a - 6b - 4)$, f) $5xy(3x - 5y + 4)$; 3a) $(2x + y)(3 - z)$, b) $(x - 5)(7x + 3)$, c) $(2y + 3z)(4x - 7t)$, d) $(3x + 2)(4x^2 - 5)$, e) $(x + 2d)(1 + 5c^2)$, f) $(5y - 2)(x - 1)$, g) $(p + 3)(q + 5)$

Factoring Trinomials of the Type $x^2 + bx + c$

Learning Objective:

a   Factor trinomials of the type $x^2 + bx + c$ by examining the constant term c.

Examples:

1. Find the two numbers that satisfy the requirements.
    a) Their product is 8 and their sum is 6.

    b) Their product is 12 and their sum is 7.

    c) Their product is –24 and their sum is –5.

    d) Their product is –18 and their sum is 3.

2. Factor.
    a) $x^2 + 3x + 2$ b) $x^2 + 6x - 8$ c) $x^2 - 6x + 8$ d) $x^2 - 10x + 9$

    e) $x^2 + x - 2$ f) $x^2 + 7x - 8$ g) $x^2 - 2x - 8$ h) $x^2 - 3x - 10$

    i) $x^2 + 12x + 35$ j) $x^2 + 2x - 48$ k) $x^2 - 11x + 24$ l) $x^2 - 4xy - 21y^2$

3. Factor out the greatest common factor. Then factor the remaining polynomial.
    a) $3x^2 + 21x + 30$ b) $5x^2 + 20x + 15$ c) $4x^2 - 8x - 96$

    d) $6x^2 + 6x - 72$ e) $3x^2 - 30xy + 48y^2$ f) $5x^2 - 20x - 105$

Teaching Notes:

- Tell students that factoring trinomials of the form $x^2 + bx + c$ is one of the most common forms of factoring they will use.
- In problems 2 and 3 many students find it helpful to make a table listing all possible factor pairs for c in the first column and their sums in the second column.
- Many students find it difficult at first to factor trinomials where the constant term is negative.
- Remind students that when the constant term is positive, the factor pairs they pick must have the same sign, while if the constant term is negative, the factor pairs must have opposite signs.
- Refer students to the *Factoring Trinomials of the Form $x^2 + bx + c$* box in the textbook.

Answers: 1a) 4 and 2, b) 4 and 3, c) –8 and 3, d) 6 and –3; 2a) (x + 2)(x + 1), b) prime, c) (x – 4)(x – 2), d) (x – 9)(x – 1), e) (x + 2)(x – 1), f) (x + 8)(x – 1), g) (x – 4)(x + 2), h) (x – 5)(x + 2), i)(x + 7)(x + 5), j) (x + 8)(x – 6), k) (x – 8)(x – 3), l) (x – 7y)(x + 3y); 3a) 3(x + 5)(x + 2), b) 5(x + 3)(x + 1), c) 4(x – 6)(x + 4), d) 6(x + 4)(x – 3), e) 3(x – 8y)(x – 2y), f) 5(x – 7)(x + 3)

Factoring $ax^2 + bx + c, a \neq 1$: The FOIL Method

Learning Objective:

a   Factor trinomials of the type $ax^2 + bx + c$, $a \neq 1$, using the FOIL method.

Examples:

1. Factor.
    a) $2x^2 + 7x + 3$

    b) $3x^2 - 2x - 8$

    c) $5x^2 - 17x + 6$

    d) $6x^2 + 19x - 20$

    e) $9x^2 + 29x + 6$

    f) $8x^2 + 18x + 9$

    g) $10y^2 + 23y + 12$

    h) $6z^2 + 5z - 6$

    i) $15z^2 - 4zx - 4x^2$

    j) $5x^2 + 3x + 2$

    k) $12 - 11a - 15a^2$

    l) $64 - 112x + 49x^2$

2. Factor out the greatest common factor from each term. Then factor the remaining trinomial.
    a) $18x^2 - 78x - 60$

    b) $10x^2 - 35x - 20$

    c) $8y^2 + 44y + 20$

    d) $-4x^2 + 10x + 6$

    e) $9x^3 - 6x^2 - 24x$

    f) $-45x^3 + 96x^2 - 48x$

Teaching Notes:

- Remind students that when the constant term is positive, the factor pairs they pick must have the same sign, while if the constant term is negative, the factor pairs must have opposite signs.
- Many students are confused at first by problem 2d). Remind them to factor out a negative as a common factor.
- Remind students to always look first for a common factor.

Answers: *1a) (2x + 1)(x + 3), b) (3x + 4)(x – 2), c) (5x – 2)(x – 3), d) (6x – 5)(x + 4), e) (9x + 2)(x + 3),*
f) (4x + 3)(2x + 3), g) (5y + 4)(2y + 3), h) (3z – 2)(2z + 3), i)(5z + 2x)(3z – 2x), j) prime, k) $(3 - 5a)(4 + 3a)$,
l) $(8 - 7x)^2$ *or* $(7x - 8)^2$; *2a) 6(3x + 2)(x – 5), b) 5(2x + 1)(x – 4), c) 4(2y + 1)(y + 5), d) –2(2x + 1)(x – 3),*
e) 3x(3x + 4)(x – 2), f) –3x(5x – 4)(3x – 4)

Factoring $ax^2 + bx + c$, $a \neq 1$: The ac-Method

Learning Objective:

a   Factor trinomials of the type $ax^2 + bx + c$, $a \neq 1$, using the ac-method.

Examples:

1. The middle term of each trinomial has been rewritten. Now factor by grouping.

    a) $x^2 + 7x + 10$ b) $b^2 + 5b - 24$ c) $6c^2 - 13c - 5$

        $= x^2 + 5x + 2x + 10$ $= b^2 - 3b + 8b - 24$ $= 6c^2 + 2c - 15c - 5$

2. Factor each trinomial using the ac-method.

    a) $2y^2 - y - 10$ b) $6m^2 + 35m - 6$ c) $12 - s - s^2$

    d) $2x^2 + 7x + 3$ e) $3x^2 - 2x - 8$ f) $5x^2 - 17x + 6$

    g) $4x^2 - 3x + 7$ h) $18y^3 + 33y^2 - 30y$ i) $5x^2 + 19xy - 4y^2$

3. Factor the following expression as described below.

    $3x^2 - x + 9x - 3$

    a) Factor by grouping the first two terms together and the last two terms together.

    b) Factor by grouping the first and third terms together and the second and fourth terms together.

    c) Do both methods give the same final answer?

Teaching Notes:

*   Many students need a quick review of factoring out a common binomial in problem 1 before attempting the factoring by grouping.
*   Most students have trouble with signs when a negative must be factored out of the second grouping, as in problem 1c). Tell them that if the two binomials that remain after the first round of factoring have opposite signs, they should try to factor a negative out of the second grouping.
*   Many students are amazed that two different grouping approaches can lead to the same final answer. Encourage them to try different groupings so that they will start to see patterns of grouping arrangements that make the factoring easier.

Answers: *1a) (x + 5)(x + 2), b) (b − 3)(b + 8), c) (3c + 1)(2c − 5); 2a) (2y − 5)(y + 2), b) (m + 6)(6m − 1), c) (3 − s)(4 + s), d)* $(2x+1)(x+3)$, *e)* $(3x+4)(x-2)$, *f)* $(5x-2)(x-3)$, *g) prime, h)* $3y(2y+5)(3y-2)$, *i)* $(5x-y)(x+4y)$; *3a) (3x − 1)(x + 3), b) (3x − 1)(x + 3), c) yes*

Factoring Trinomial Squares and Differences of Squares

Learning Objectives:

    a   Recognize trinomial squares.
    b   Factor trinomial squares.
    c   Recognize differences of squares.
    d   Factor differences of squares, being careful to factor completely.

Examples:

1. Determine whether each of the following is a trinomial square, a difference of two squares, or neither.

    a) $x^2 - 5x + 25$
    b) $x^2 - 16$
    c) $y^2 - 16y + 64$

    d) $25x^2 + 49$
    e) $100m^2 - 9$
    f) $16k^2 + 40k + 25$

2. Factor completely.

    a) $x^2 - 4$
    b) $x^2 - 49$
    c) $9x^2 - 25$
    d) $25x^2 - 49y^2$

    e) $100 - x^2$
    f) $81x^4 - 1$
    g) $81x^2 - y^2$
    h) $x^4 - 4$

3. Factor completely.

    a) $x^2 + 18x + 81$
    b) $x^2 + 2x + 1$
    c) $x^2 + 12x + 36$

    d) $4x^2 - 28x + 49$
    e) $49x^2 - 42xy + 9y^2$
    f) $16x^2 + 72xy + 81y^2$

4. Factor completely. Look first for a common factor.

    a) $4x^2 - 16$
    b) $72x^2 - 98y^2$
    c) $ab^2 - 16a$

    d) $18x^2 + 12x + 2$
    e) $75x^2 + 90x + 27$
    f) $125x^2 - 150x + 45$

Teaching Notes:

- Some students understand the difference of squares formula, $A^2 - B^2 = (A+B)(A-B)$, better if 2a) and 2b) are first done using trinomial factoring (with a $0x$ middle term).
- Encourage students to become proficient with special case factoring as it will be important for future algebra topics such as completing the square.

Factoring: A General Strategy

Learning Objective:

a   Factor polynomials completely using any of the methods considered in this chapter.

Examples:

1. Factor completely.

   a) $2x^2 + 6x + 4$ b) $3x^2 - 2x - 8$ c) $25x^2 - 100$

   d) $10x^2 - 35x - 20$ e) $9x^2 + 24xy + 16y^2$ f) $-x^2 - 2x + 48$

   g) $9x^2 + 12x + 4$ h) $xy + 2y - 3x - 6$ i) $x^2 + 3x - 5$

   j) $2x^2 + 5xy - 12y^2$ k) $-5x^7 - 30x^5 + 10x^4$ l) $16 - a^8$

   m) $y^2 - y - 20$ n) $4x^2 + 81$ o) $p^2 - p + \dfrac{1}{4}$

Teaching Notes:

- Refer students to the Factoring Strategy box in the text.
- Encourage students to be organized in their approach to factoring and to keep track of products they have tried.

Answers: *1a)* $2(x+2)(x+1)$, *b)* $(3x+4)(x-2)$, *c)* $25(x+2)(x-2)$, *d)* $5(2x+1)(x-4)$, *e)* $(3x+4y)^2$, *f)* $-(x+8)(x-6)$, *g)* $(3x+2)^2$, *h)* $(x+2)(y-3)$, *i) prime, j)* $(2x-3y)(x+4y)$, *k)* $-5x^4(x^3+6x-2)$, *l)* $(4+a^4)(2+a^2)(2-a^2)$, *m)* $(y-5)(y+4)$, *n) prime, o)* $\left(p-\dfrac{1}{2}\right)^2$

Solving Quadratic Equations by Factoring

Learning Objectives:

    a   Solve equations (already factored) using the principle of zero products.
    b   Solve quadratic equations by factoring and then using the principle of zero products.

Examples:

1. Solve using the principle of zero products.

    a) $3 \cdot x = 0$ b) $2(x - 5) = 0$ c) $x(x + 6) = 0$

    d) $(x-4)(x+9)=0$ e) $(2x - 3)(4x + 5) = 0$ f) $(x-2)(x+4)(5x-6)=0$

2. Solve by factoring and using the principle of zero products. Remember to check.

    a) $x^2 + 9x - 36 = 0$ b) $9x^2 - 2x = 0$

    c) $3x^2 - 21x + 30 = 0$ d) $5x^2 - 3x - 8 = 0$

    e) $x^2 - x = 6$ f) $x^2 - 64 = 63x$

    g) $x(3x + 13) = 10$ h) $(x - 3)(x + 4) = -4(x + 4)$

    i) $81a^2 = 16$ j) $15x^2 - x - 6 = 0$

Teaching Notes:

- Remind students to always get zero on one side before factoring.
- Some students try to use the principle of zero products before the equation is in the proper form. For example, in 2e) some students incorrectly reason $x^2 - x = 6 \rightarrow x(x-1) = 6 \rightarrow x = 6,\ x-1 = 6$ etc.

Answers: 1a) 0, b) 5, c) $-6,0$, d) $-9,4$, e) $-\dfrac{5}{4},\dfrac{3}{2}$, f) $-4,\dfrac{6}{5},2$; 2a) $-12,3$, b) $0,\dfrac{2}{9}$, c) 2,5, d) $-1,\dfrac{8}{5}$,

e) $-2,3$, f) $-1,64$, g) $-5,\dfrac{2}{3}$, h) $-4,-1$, i) $-\dfrac{4}{9},\dfrac{4}{9}$, j) $-\dfrac{3}{5},\dfrac{2}{3}$

Applications of Quadratic Equations

Learning Objective:

   a   Solve applied problems involving quadratic equations that can be solved by factoring.

Examples:

1.   The area of a circle is 144π square meters. Find its radius.

2. The width of a rectangle is 9 kilometers less than twice its length. If its area is 56 square kilometers, find the dimensions of the rectangle.

3.   The product of two consecutive even integers is 14 more than 7 times their sum. Find the integers.

4.   Find the lengths of the sides of the triangle.

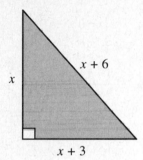

5. A window washer accidentally drops a bucket from the top of a 144-ft building. The height, h, of the bucket after t seconds is given by $h = -16t^2 + 144$. When will the bucket hit the ground?

Teaching Notes:

- Many students find these problems difficult.
- Refer students to the *Five-Step Problem-Solving Process* in the text.
- Encourage students to make a diagram whenever possible.
- Many students find the applied problems difficult and need to see many examples.
- Remind students to check whether their answers are reasonable for applied problems.

Answers: 1) radius = 12 m; 2) length = 8 km and width = 7 km; 3) 14 and 16 or –2 and 0;
4) x = 9, x+3 = 12, and x+6 = 15; 5) after 3 sec

Multiplying and Simplifying Rational Expressions

Learning Objectives:

   a   Find all numbers for which a rational expression is not defined.

   b   Multiply a rational expression by 1, using an expression such as A/A.

   c   Simplify rational expressions by factoring the numerator and the denominator and removing factors of 1.

   d   Multiply rational expressions and simplify.

Examples:

1. Find all numbers for which each rational expression is not defined.

    a) $\dfrac{3}{x}$ b) $\dfrac{5x}{x-2}$ c) $\dfrac{x-3}{x^2+x-12}$ d) $\dfrac{y+3}{6}$

2. Multiply.

    a) $\dfrac{3x^2}{3x^2}\cdot\dfrac{5x^4}{8y^2}$ b) $\dfrac{x+3}{x+3}\cdot\dfrac{x^2-4}{x^2+6}$

3. Simplify.

    a) $\dfrac{9x}{12x^5}$ b) $\dfrac{m-n}{n-m}$ c) $\dfrac{2x-12}{3x-18}$

    d) $\dfrac{9x^2+27x^3}{3}$ e) $\dfrac{12-6x}{4x-8}$ f) $\dfrac{12xy^2}{9x^2y^2(y+3x)}$

    g) $\dfrac{x^2-3x-10}{x^2-4x-12}$ h) $\dfrac{-4x-4}{20x^2+28x+8}$ i) $\dfrac{25-x^2}{2x^2-7x-15}$

4. Multiply and simplify.

    a) $\dfrac{12x^4}{5x}\cdot\dfrac{10y}{3x^2}$ b) $\dfrac{x+2}{x}\cdot\dfrac{x^2+3x}{x^2-x-6}$ c) $\dfrac{x^2-2x-3}{x^2-x-6}\cdot\dfrac{x^2-2x-8}{x^2-3x-4}$

    d) $\dfrac{x^4-1}{(x-1)^3}\cdot\dfrac{x^2-1}{(x+1)^3}$ e) $\dfrac{x^2+x-12}{x^2-16}\cdot\dfrac{x-4}{6-2x}$ f) $\dfrac{5a^2}{2a^2+3a-2}\cdot\dfrac{4a-2}{15a}$

Teaching Notes:

- Students must be very comfortable with factoring techniques to succeed here.
- Many students have trouble with problems such as 3b), where the factors in the numerator and denominator are opposite signs. They might need to see a few more examples of how to handle the situation.
- A common error in 3g) is canceling the x out of the final answer.

Answers: *1a)* $x=0$, *b)* $x=2$, *c)* $x=-4$ *and* $x=3$, *d) none;* *2a)* $\dfrac{(3x^2)(5x^4)}{(3x^2)(8y^2)}$, *b)* $\dfrac{(x+3)(x^2-4)}{(x+3)(x^2+6)}$;

3a) $\dfrac{3}{4x^4}$, *b)* -1, *c)* $\dfrac{2}{3}$, *d)* $3x^2+9x^3$, *e)* $-\dfrac{3}{2}$, *f)* $\dfrac{4}{3x(y+3x)}$, *g)* $\dfrac{x-5}{x-6}$, *h)* $\dfrac{-1}{5x+2}$, *i)* $\dfrac{-(5+x)}{2x+3}$; *4a)* $8xy$,

b) $\dfrac{x+3}{x-3}$, *c)* 1, *d)* $\dfrac{x^2+1}{(x-1)(x+1)}$, *e)* $-\dfrac{1}{2}$, *f)* $\dfrac{2a}{3(a+2)}$

Division and Reciprocals

Learning Objectives:

    a   Find the reciprocal of a rational expression.
    b   Divide rational expressions and simplify.

Examples:

1. Find the reciprocal.

    a) $\dfrac{5}{x}$ b) $\dfrac{m+2}{m-3}$ c) a^2-b^2 d) $\dfrac{1}{2x+2y}$ e) $\dfrac{x^2+6x+5}{x^2-4x-5}$

2. Divide and simplify.

    a) $\dfrac{3}{4} \div \dfrac{9}{16}$ b) $\dfrac{6}{x} \div \dfrac{12}{x}$

    c) $\dfrac{6p-6}{p} \div \dfrac{7p-7}{9p^2}$ d) $\dfrac{x^2+5x+6}{x^2+10x+21} \div \dfrac{x^2+2x}{x^2+16x+63}$

    e) $\dfrac{(x-11)^2}{2} \div \dfrac{2x-22}{4}$ f) $\dfrac{x^2-16x+60}{x-10} \div (x-6)$

    g) $\dfrac{3x^2+6xy+3y^2}{x^2+4xy+3y^2} \div \dfrac{4x+4y}{x+3y}$ h) $\dfrac{x^2-4x+3}{x^2-12x+20} \div \dfrac{x^2-10x+9}{x^2-19x+90}$

    i) $\dfrac{5m^2-40m+75}{15m-75} \div \dfrac{m^2+6m+9}{6m^2-36m+54}$

Teaching Notes:

- Many students need a review of multiplying and dividing fractions before attempting to divide rational expressions.
- Most students who are comfortable with factoring do not find this section difficult once they are reminded of the rules for multiplying and dividing.

Answers: _1a)_ $\dfrac{x}{5}$, _b)_ $\dfrac{m-3}{m+2}$, _c)_ $\dfrac{1}{a^2-b^2}$, _d)_ $2x+2y$, _e)_ $\dfrac{x^2-4x-5}{x^2+6x+5}$; _2a)_ $\dfrac{4}{3}$, _b)_ $\dfrac{1}{2}$, _c)_ $\dfrac{54p}{7}$, _d)_ $\dfrac{x+9}{x}$,

_e)_ $x-11$, _f)_ _1_, _g)_ $\dfrac{3}{4}$, _h)_ $\dfrac{x-3}{x-2}$, _i)_ $\dfrac{2(m-3)^3}{(m+3)^2}$

Least Common Multiples and Denominators

Learning Objectives:

    a   Find the LCM of several numbers by factoring.
    b   Add fractions, first finding the LCD.
    c   Find the LCM of algebraic expressions by factoring.

Examples:

1. Find the LCM.
   a) $8, 12$ b) $3, 5$ c) $12, 16, 24$

2. Add, first finding the LCD. Simplify if possible.
   a) $\dfrac{5}{24} + \dfrac{2}{9}$ b) $\dfrac{1}{3} + \dfrac{7}{50}$ c) $\dfrac{2}{5} + \dfrac{1}{4} + \dfrac{4}{15}$

3. Find the LCM.
   a) $5x^3, \ 20x^5$ b) $32m, \ 48m$ c) $27t^3, \ 36t$

   d) $24y^2, \ 14y - 20$ e) $e - f, f - e$ f) $2c^2 - 9c + 10, \ 2c^2 + c - 15$

   g) $4xy, \ 5x^2y^2$ h) $m^2 - 4m, \ m^2 - 6m + 8$ i) $x^2 - 2x - 15, \ x^2 - 10x + 25$

Teaching Notes:

- Students have trouble with this section.
- Refer students to the ***Finding the Least Common Multiple (LCM)*** box in the text.

Answers: *1a) 24, b) 15, c) 48;* *2a)* $\dfrac{31}{72}$*, b)* $\dfrac{71}{150}$*, c)* $\dfrac{11}{12}$*;* *3a)* $20x^5$*, b)* $96m$*, c)* $108t^3$*, d)* $24y^2(7y - 10)$*,*

e) $e - f$ or $f - e$, f) $(2c - 5)(c - 2)(c + 3)$, g) $20x^2y^2$, h) $m(m - 2)(m - 4)$, i) $(x + 3)(x - 5)^2$

Adding Rational Expressions

Learning Objective:

   a   Add rational expressions.

Examples:

1. Add. Simplify if possible.

   a) $\dfrac{1}{4}+\dfrac{2}{4}$ b) $\dfrac{1}{6}+\dfrac{4}{9}$ c) $\dfrac{4}{3}+\dfrac{2}{-3}$

2. Add. Simplify if possible.

   a) $\dfrac{7x+4}{9x+6}+\dfrac{x-2}{9x+6}$ b) $\dfrac{m^2-11m}{m-5}+\dfrac{30}{-5+m}$ c) $\dfrac{6}{x^2}+\dfrac{4}{x}$

   d) $\dfrac{6}{m^2n^3}+\dfrac{-5}{8mn^2}$ e) $\dfrac{k}{k-4}+\dfrac{k-4}{k}$ f) $\dfrac{4z+5}{z-2}+\dfrac{3z}{2-z}$

   g) $\dfrac{x-4}{2x+3}+\dfrac{x+1}{3x+2}$ h) $\dfrac{x-4}{x^2+5x+6}+\dfrac{5x+6}{x^2+4x+3}$ i) $\dfrac{3}{x^2-3x+2}+\dfrac{7}{x^2-1}$

Teaching Notes:

- Many students need the review of fractions in problem 1.
- Show students how to build the LCDs of the fractions and rational expressions by using prime factorizations. Even though that method is not always necessary with fractions, many students have trouble finding the LCD of a rational expression and understand it better after seeing this.
- Remind students to factor the resulting numerator if possible and to leave the denominator in factored form in order to identify factors of 1 which may be removed.

Answers: *1a)* $\dfrac{3}{4}$, *b)* $\dfrac{11}{18}$, *c)* $\dfrac{2}{3}$;   *2a)* $\dfrac{8x+2}{9x+6}$, *b)* $m-6$, *c)* $\dfrac{4x+6}{x^2}$, *d)* $\dfrac{48-5mn}{8m^2n^3}$, *e)* $\dfrac{2k^2-8k+16}{k(k-4)}$,

f) $\dfrac{z+5}{z-2}$, *g)* $\dfrac{5(x^2-x-1)}{(2x+3)(3x+2)}$, *h)* $\dfrac{6x^2+13x+8}{(x+1)(x+2)(x+3)}$, *i)* $\dfrac{10x-11}{(x+1)(x-1)(x-2)}$

Subtracting Rational Expressions

Learning Objectives:

a   Subtract rational expressions.
b   Simplify combined additions and subtractions of rational expressions.

Examples:

1. Subtract. Simplify if possible.

a) $\dfrac{9}{y} - \dfrac{5}{y}$

b) $\dfrac{x}{x-5} - \dfrac{5}{x-5}$

c) $\dfrac{m+3}{7} - \dfrac{m-2}{6}$

d) $\dfrac{4x+3y}{2x^2 y} - \dfrac{8x+y}{xy^2}$

e) $\dfrac{6x-16}{x-2} - \dfrac{4x-7}{x-2}$

f) $\dfrac{6-x}{x-8} - \dfrac{5x-2}{8-x}$

g) $\dfrac{4}{x-3} - \dfrac{6}{x+3}$

h) $\dfrac{14x}{x^2-16} - \dfrac{x}{x-4}$

i) $\dfrac{x}{x^2-16} - \dfrac{6}{x^2+5x+4}$

2. Perform the indicated operations and simplify.

a) $\dfrac{6(x+4)}{x-5} - \dfrac{2(2x+3)}{5-x} + \dfrac{4x+1}{x-5}$

b) $\dfrac{a+2}{a^2-9} - \dfrac{a+5}{a+3} + \dfrac{a-4}{3-a}$

c) $\dfrac{6y}{y^2-1} - \dfrac{3}{y+1} - \dfrac{3}{y}$

Teaching Notes:

- Show students how to build the LCDs of the fractions by using prime factorizations. Even though that method is not always necessary with fractions, many students have trouble finding the LCD of rational expressions and understand it better after seeing this.
- Remind students to watch the signs when subtracting, especially if the numerator of the term being subtracted is not a monomial.

Answers: 1a) $\dfrac{4}{y}$, b) 1, c) $\dfrac{32-m}{42}$, d) $\dfrac{-16x^2+2xy+3y^2}{2x^2 y^2}$, e) $\dfrac{2x-9}{x-2}$, f) $\dfrac{4(x+1)}{x-8}$, g) $\dfrac{2(15-x)}{(x-3)(x+3)}$

h) $\dfrac{-x(x-10)}{(x-4)(x+4)}$, i) $\dfrac{x^2-5x+24}{(x+1)(x+4)(x-4)}$; 2a) $\dfrac{14x+31}{x-5}$, b) $\dfrac{-2x^2+29}{(x-3)(x+3)}$, c) $\dfrac{3}{y(y-1)(y+1)}$

Solving Rational Equations

Learning Objective:

a   Solve rational equations.

Examples:

1. Solve and check.

   a) $\dfrac{3}{4} - \dfrac{2}{3} = \dfrac{x}{24}$

   b) $\dfrac{2}{5} + \dfrac{7}{8} = \dfrac{1}{x}$

2. Solve and check.

   a) $\dfrac{15}{x} = 4 - \dfrac{1}{x}$

   b) $x + 1 = \dfrac{12}{x}$

   c) $\dfrac{5-a}{a} + \dfrac{3}{4} = \dfrac{7}{a}$

   d) $\dfrac{2}{x} = \dfrac{x}{5x-12}$

   e) $\dfrac{3}{y+5} - \dfrac{5}{y-5} = \dfrac{6}{y^2-25}$

3. Solve and check. If there is no solution, so indicate.

   a) $\dfrac{2}{x+3} = 5 + \dfrac{2}{x+3}$

   b) $\dfrac{x}{2x+2} = \dfrac{-2x}{4x+4} + \dfrac{2x-3}{x+1}$

   c) $\dfrac{6x}{x+5} - \dfrac{30}{x-5} = \dfrac{6x^2+150}{x^2-25}$

   d) $\dfrac{2}{x+3} = \dfrac{1}{x+6} - \dfrac{6}{x^2+9x+18}$

Teaching Notes:

- Remind students to always check the possible solutions when solving a rational equation. Some possible solutions make a denominator in the original equation equal 0.
- Some students prefer to make equivalent rational expressions with a common denominator, and then set the numerators equal to each other.
- Refer students to the *Solving Rational Equations* box in the textbook.

Answers: *1a) 2, b)* $\dfrac{40}{51}$; *2a) 4, b) −4, 3, c) −8, d) 4, 6, e) −23 ; 3a) no solution, b) 3, c) no solution, d) −15*

Applications Using Rational Equations and Proportions

Learning Objectives:

    a   Solve applied problems using rational equations.
    b   Solve proportion problems.

Examples:

1. A painter can finish painting a house in 7 hours. His assistant takes 9 hours to finish the same job. How long would it take them to complete the job if they were working together?

2. A cyclist bikes at a constant speed for 22 miles. He then returns home at the same speed but takes a different route. His return trip takes one hour longer and is 27 miles. Find his speed.

3. Write a ratio for each of the following. Write fractions in lowest terms. Simplify if possible.
    a) 30 lb to 50 guests   b) 20 min to 2 hr

4. Jeff traveled 26.2 mi in 3 hr. What is his speed in miles per hour?

5. Solve and check.
    a) A quality control inspector found 4 defective computer chips in a shipment of 500 computer chips. At this rate, how many computer chips would be defective in a shipment of 2000 computer chips?

    b) A caterer estimates that 6 gallons of punch will serve 40 people. How much *additional* punch would be required to serve 60 people?

6. Find the missing length in the similar triangles.

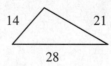
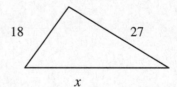

Teaching Notes:

- Many students find this section difficult.
- Most students benefit by setting up a chart to solve distance and work problems.
- Encourage students to draw and label a diagram and to list any relevant formulas whenever possible.

Answers: *1a)* $3\dfrac{15}{16}$ *hr; 2) 5 mph; 3a)* $\dfrac{3}{5}$ *lb/guest, b) 10 min/hr; 4) 8.7$\overline{3}$ mph; 5a) 16 computer chips, b) 3 gal; 6) x = 36*

Complex Rational Expressions

Learning Objective:

   a   Simplify complex rational expressions.

Examples:

1. Simplify.

   a) $\dfrac{\frac{2}{7}}{\frac{4}{9}}$
                                 b) $\dfrac{\frac{1}{5}}{\frac{2}{3}+\frac{7}{15}}$

2. Simplify by multiplying by the LCM of all the denominators (Method 1).

   a) $\dfrac{\frac{1}{x}-\frac{1}{y}}{\frac{1}{xy}}$
          b) $\dfrac{\frac{5}{x}}{\frac{9}{x+2}}$
          c) $\dfrac{4+\frac{2}{x}}{\frac{x}{3}+\frac{1}{6}}$

   d) $\dfrac{\frac{5}{9x-1}-5}{\frac{5}{9x-1}+5}$
          e) $\dfrac{\frac{4}{x+5}}{\frac{1}{x-5}-\frac{2}{x^2-25}}$
       f) $\dfrac{\frac{x}{x+2}+2}{\frac{x^2-1}{x-1}}$

3. Simplify by adding or subtracting in the numerator and the denominator (Method 2). Use the same a) through f) in Example 2 above.

Teaching Note:

- Refer students to the boxes for Method 1 and Method 2 for simplifying complex rational expressions in the textbook.

Answers: *1a) 9/14, b) 3/17; 2a) y − x, b) $\dfrac{5x+10}{9x}$, c) 12/x, d) $\dfrac{-9x+2}{9x}$, e) $\dfrac{4x-20}{x+3}$, f) $\dfrac{3x+4}{(x+1)(x+2)}$;*

3a)–f) same answers as 2a)–f)

Direct Variation and Inverse Variation

Learning Objectives:

    a   Find an equation of direct variation given a pair of values of the variables.
    b   Solve applied problems involving direct variation.
    c   Find an equation of inverse variation given a pair of values of the variables.
    d   Solve applied problems involving inverse variation.

Examples:

1. Find an equation of variation if x varies directly as y, and $x = 2$ when $y = 5$. Then find x when $y = 10$.

2. Find an equation of variation if c varies directly as d, and $c = 9$ when $c = 11$. Then find c when $d = 33$.

3. Find an equation of variation if r varies inversely as s, and $r = 14$ when $s = 4$. Then find r when $s = 7$.

4. Find an equation of variation if g varies inversely as h, and $g = 3$ when $h = 48$. Then find g when $h = 2$.

5. The interest on a money market account varies directly as the rate of interest. If the interest is \$450 when the interest rate is 6%, find the interest when the rate is $3\frac{1}{2}$%.

6. If the fuel efficiency of your car, in miles per gallon (mpg), varies inversely with your average driving speed, in miles per hour (mph), and you get 30 miles per gallon when driving at an average speed of 50 mph, what will your fuel efficiency be when you drive at an average speed of 60 mph?

Teaching Notes:

- Many students find this section difficult.
- Refer students to the *Direct Variation* and *Inverse Variation* boxes in the text.

Answers: 1) $y = \frac{5}{2}x$, $x = 4$; 2) $c = \frac{9}{11}d$, $c = 27$; 3) $r = \frac{56}{s}$, $r = 8$; 4) $g = \frac{144}{x}$, $g = 72$; 5) \$262.50;
6) *25 mpg*

Systems of Equations in Two Variables

Learning Objectives:

    a   Determine whether an ordered pair is a solution of a system of equations.
    b   Solve systems of two linear equations in two variables by graphing.

Examples:

1. Determine whether the given ordered pair is a solution of the given system of linear equations.

   a) Is $(4,-1)$ a solution of the system $\begin{array}{l} 2x - y = 3, \\ x + y = 3 \end{array}$?

   b) Is $(-2,5)$ a solution of the system $\begin{array}{l} 2x + 3y = 11, \\ 5x - 2y = -20 \end{array}$?

2. Draw an example of each system of equations and discuss whether there are any intersection points, and if so, how many.
   a) two straight lines with different slopes; number of intersection points = ___

   b) two straight lines with the same slope but different y-intercept values; number of intersection points = ___

   c) two straight lines with the same slope and same y-intercept value; number of intersection points = ___

3. Solve by graphing. Each system has a unique solution.

   a) $\begin{array}{l} x - y = 2, \\ x + y = 4 \end{array}$

   b) $\begin{array}{l} -2x + 2y = 6, \\ 4x + 2y = 18 \end{array}$

   c) $\frac{1}{3}x - y = 1; \; x = 3$

4. Solve by graphing. Each system has either no solution or an infinite number of solutions.

   a) $\begin{array}{l} x + y = 3, \\ 2x + 2y = 6 \end{array}$

   b) $\begin{array}{l} 2x + y = 5, \\ 2x + y = 8 \end{array}$

   c) $\begin{array}{l} y - 5x = 2, \\ 5y = 25x + 10 \end{array}$

   d) $\begin{array}{l} x = -y, \\ x + y = 6 \end{array}$

Teaching Note:

- Encourage students to be neat with their graphs.

Answers: 1a) no, b) yes; 2a) 1, b) 0, c) infinite number of solutions. See graph answer pages. Graphs may vary; 3a) $(3,1)$, b) $(2,5)$, c) $(3,0)$, see graph answer pages; 4a) infinite number of solutions, b) no solution, c) infinite number of solutions, d) no solution, see graph answer pages

The Substitution Method

Learning Objectives:

   a   Solve a system of two equations in two variables by the substitution method when one of the equations has a variable alone on one side.

   b   Solve a system of two equations in two variables by the substitution method when neither equation has a variable alone on one side.

   c   Solve applied problems by translating to a system of two equations and then solving using the substitution method.

Examples:

1. Find the solution to each system of equations by the substitution method. Check your answers. Place your solution in the form (x, y).

    a) $x + y = 6,$ b) $x = 6y - 18,$ c) $-2x + 6y = -12,$
        $x = y - 2$ $2x - 7y = -16$ $x = -5y + 6$

    d) $x - y = 10,$ e) $-5x - 2y = -15,$
        $y = -x - 2$ $y = 8x - 3$

2. Find the solution to each system of equations using the substitution method. First solve one equation for one variable. Place your answer in the form (x, y).

    a) $x - y = 4,$ b) $-4x + y = -23,$ c) $3x + 2y = 1,$
        $x + y = 8$ $8x + 3y = -29$ $2x + y = 0$

    d) $8x + 5y = -3,$ e) $6x + 5y = 25,$
       $-2x + 3y = 5$ $4x - 3y = -15$

3. The perimeter of a table cloth is 30 ft. The length is 3 ft less than twice the width. Find the dimensions of the table cloth.

Teaching Notes:

- Remind students that a solution must be checked in both original equations.
- Many students write the solution as x = a number and y = a number, instead of in the form (x, y).
- Remind students that after they solve for the first variable, they must solve for the second variable in order to get a complete solution.

Answers: *1a)* $(2,4)$, *b)* $(6,4)$, *c)* $(6,0)$, *d)* $(4,-6)$, *e)* $(1,5)$; *2a)* $(6,2)$, *b)* $(2,-15)$, *c)* $(-1,2)$, *d)* $(-1,1)$, *e)* $(0,5)$; *3) length = 9 ft, width = 6 ft*

The Elimination Method

Learning Objectives:

   a   Solve a system of two equations in two variables using the elimination method when no multiplication is necessary.

   b   Solve a system of two equations in two variables using the elimination method when multiplication is necessary.

Examples:

1. Solve using the elimination method.

   a) $x + y = -12,$
      $x - y = 2$

   b) $-x - 8y = 15,$
      $7x + 8y = 39$

   c) $7x - y = 19,$
      $x + y = -3$

   d) $5x - 3y = 9,$
      $-5x + 3y = -9$

   e) $3x + 2y = 28,$
      $x - 2y = -4$

   f) $0.1x + y = 1,$
      $-0.1x + 0.5y = 2$

2. Solve using the multiplication principle first.

   a) $x + 7y = -53,$
      $-5x + 6y = -22$

   b) $9x + 8y = 72,$
      $-7x - 4y = -56$

   c) $9x - 7y = 44,$
      $6x + 2y = -4$

   d) $9x + 7y = -14,$
      $-7x + 2y = -4$

   e) $\frac{1}{2}x + \frac{1}{2}y = -3,$
      $x - y = 8$

   f) $\frac{3x}{8} - \frac{3y}{5} = \frac{33}{80},$
      $\frac{4x}{7} + \frac{4y}{5} = \frac{37}{35}$

   g) $4x = -3y,$
      $5x + 4y = -1$

   h) $-0.1x + 0.6y = 1.3,$
      $0.8x + 0.6y = -5$

   i) $3x - 5y = -15,$
      $-6x + 10y = -30$

Teaching Notes:

- Encourage students to discuss which variable is easier to eliminate, and by what number an equation should be multiplied to make the elimination possible.
- Many students find problems with decimal numbers or fractions difficult. Remind them to start by multiplying both sides of the equations by the LCD or the appropriate power of 10 to clear fractions or decimals. Then the system has integer coefficients.

Answers: *1a)* $(-5, -7)$, *b)* $(9, -3)$, *c)* $(2, -5)$, *d) infinite number of solutions, e)* $(6, 5)$, *f)* $(-10, 2)$;

2a) $(-4, -7)$, *b)* $(8, 0)$, *c)* $(1, -5)$, *d)* $(0, -2)$, *e)* $(1, -7)$, *f)* $\left(\frac{3}{2}, \frac{1}{4}\right)$, *g)* $(3, -4)$, *h)* $(-7, 1)$, *i) no solution*

Applications and Problem Solving

Learning Objective:

a   Solve applied problems by translating to a system of two equations in two variables.

Examples:

1. *Numbers* Two numbers total –6, and their difference is 12. Find the two numbers.

2. *Ticket Cost* Dillon purchased tickets to an air show for 4 adults and 2 children. The total cost was $86. The cost of a child's ticket was $5 less than the cost of an adult's ticket. Find the price of an adult's ticket and a child's ticket.

3. *Coins* Jason always throws loose change into a pencil holder on his desk and takes it out every two weeks. This time it is all nickels and dimes. There are 7 times as many dimes as nickels, and the value of the coins is $4.50. How many nickels and dimes does Jason have?

4. *Mixture* Kelly is a partner in an internet-based seed and garden supply business. The company offers a blend of exotic wildflower seeds for $95 per pound and a blend of common wildflower seeds for $20 per pound. Kelly is creating a medium-price product by mixing together 30 pounds of the more expensive blend with 10 pounds of the less expensive blend. What will be the price per pound for the new blend? (Round to the nearest cent, if necessary.)

Teaching Notes:

- Many students find this section difficult.
- Remind students to use the *five-step problem-solving strategy*.
- Encourage students to draw and label diagrams or construct charts whenever appropriate.
- Encourage students to discuss which algebraic method, substitution or elimination, is easiest to apply for each system.

Answers: *1) 3, –9; 2) adult $16, child $11; 3) 6 nickels, 42 dimes; 4) $76.25 per pound*

Applications with Motion

Learning Objective:

a   Solve motion problems using the formula $d = rt$.

Examples:

1.   A 520-mile trip from one city to another takes 4 hours when a plane is flying with the wind. The return trip against the wind takes 5 hours. Find the speed of the plane in still air and the speed of the wind.

2.   Julie and Eric row their boat (at a constant rate) 16 miles downstream for 2 hours, helped by the current. Rowing at the same rate, the trip back against the current takes 8 hours. Find the speed of the current.

3.   Two cars leave a town at the same time heading in the same direction. One travels 60 mph and the other travels 52 mph. In how many hours will they be 80 mi apart?

Teaching Notes:

- Many students find this section difficult.
- Remind students to use the *five-step problem-solving strategy*.
- Encourage students to draw and label diagrams or construct charts whenever appropriate.
- Encourage students to discuss which algebraic method, substitution or elimination, is easiest to apply for each system.

Answers: *1) speed of plane in still air is 117 mph, speed of wind is 13 mph; 2) 3 mph; 3) 10 hr*

Introduction to Radical Expressions

Learning Objectives:

    a   Find the principal square roots and their opposites of the whole numbers from 0^2 to 25^2.
    b   Approximate square roots of real numbers using a calculator.
    c   Solve applied problems involving square roots.
    d   Identify radicands of radical expressions.
    e   Determine whether a radical expression represents a real number.
    f   Simplify a radical expression with a perfect-square radicand.

Examples:

1. Find the square roots.
    a) 9   b) 25   c) 36   d) 49   e) 100

2. Simplify.
    a) $\sqrt{4}$ b) $-\sqrt{4}$ c) $\sqrt{25}$ d) $-\sqrt{121}$ e) $\sqrt{169}$

3. Use a calculator to approximate to three decimal places.
    a) $\sqrt{5}$ b) $-\sqrt{7}$ c) $\sqrt{59}$ d) $-\sqrt{951}$

4. Identify the radicand.
    a) $\sqrt{500}$ b) $\sqrt{y}+2$ c) $4\sqrt{x^2+2}$

5. Determine whether each expression represents a real number. Answer yes or no.
    a) $\sqrt{-4}$ b) $-\sqrt{121}$ c) $-\sqrt{-64}$

6. Simplify. Assume that radicands do not represent the square of a negative number.
    a) $\sqrt{m^2}$ b) $\sqrt{25x^2}$ c) $\sqrt{(7n)^2}$ d) $\sqrt{9x^2+6x+1}$

Teaching Notes:

- Many students find the signs confusing with these problems.
- Although the square root of a negative number is included here, it is mentioned only briefly in the text and need not be a major focal point.
- Encourage students to memorize the squares of the numbers 0 through 25.

Answers: *1a) 3, –3, b) 5, –5, c) 6, –6, d) 7, –7, e) 10, –10; 2a) 2, b) –2, c) 5, d) -11, e) 13; 3a) 2.236, b) –2.646, c) 7.681, d) –30.838; 4a) 500, b) y, c) x^2+2 ; 5a) no, b) yes, c) no; 6a) m, b) 5x, c) 7n, d) 3x+1*

Multiplying and Simplifying with Radical Expressions

Learning Objectives:

    a   Simplify radical expressions.
    b   Simplify radical expressions where radicands are powers.
    c   Multiply radical expressions and, if possible, simplify.

Examples:

1. Simplify by factoring. Recall that we have assumed that no radicands were formed by raising negative quantities to even powers.

   a) $\sqrt{8}$ b) $-\sqrt{18}$ c) $\sqrt{72}$ d) $\sqrt{147}$

   e) $\sqrt{16x}$ f) $\sqrt{28y^2}$ g) $\sqrt{x^2-10x+25}$ h) $\sqrt{208}$

2. Simplify by factoring.

   a) $\sqrt{x^4}$ b) $\sqrt{x^6}$ c) $\sqrt{x^3}$ d) $\sqrt{x^7}$

   e) $\sqrt{(y+8)^5}$ f) $\sqrt{25(y+4)^{12}}$ g) $\sqrt{80x^3}$ h) $\sqrt{128x^6y^8}$

3. Multiply and then, if possible, simplify by factoring.

   a) $\sqrt{5}\cdot\sqrt{7}$ b) $\sqrt{6}\cdot\sqrt{3}$ c) $\sqrt{11}\cdot\sqrt{11}$ d) $\sqrt{15x}\cdot\sqrt{21y}$

   e) $\sqrt{3}\sqrt{2n-6}$ f) $\sqrt{mn}\sqrt{np}$ g) $\sqrt{x+3}\sqrt{x+3}$ h) $\sqrt{24x^2y^3z^5}\sqrt{2x^3yz^7}$

Teaching Notes:

- Encourage students to write non-perfect square numbers as the product of the largest possible perfect square and another number.
- Most students need a lot of practice finding square roots of variables with odd exponents.
- Refer students to the **Product Rule for Radicals** box in the textbook.

Answers: _1a)_ $2\sqrt{2}$ _, b)_ $-3\sqrt{2}$ _, c)_ $6\sqrt{2}$ _, d)_ $7\sqrt{3}$ _, e)_ $4\sqrt{x}$ _, f)_ $2y\sqrt{7}$ _, g)_ $x-5$ _, h)_ $4\sqrt{13}$; _2a)_ x^2 _, b)_ x^3 ,
_c)_ $x\sqrt{x}$ _, d)_ $x^3\sqrt{x}$ _, e)_ $(y+8)^2\sqrt{y+8}$ _, f)_ $5(y+4)^6$ _, g)_ $4x\sqrt{5x}$ _, h)_ $8x^3y^4\sqrt{2}$; _3a)_ $\sqrt{35}$ _, b)_ $3\sqrt{2}$ _, c)_ 11,
_d)_ $3\sqrt{35xy}$ _, e)_ $\sqrt{6n-18}$ _, f)_ $n\sqrt{mp}$ _, g)_ $x+3$ _, h)_ $4x^2y^2z^6\sqrt{3x}$

Quotients Involving Radical Expressions

Learning Objectives:

- a   Divide radical expressions.
- b   Simplify square roots of quotients.
- c   Rationalize the denominator of a radical expression.

Examples:

1. Divide and simplify.

   a) $\dfrac{\sqrt{20}}{\sqrt{45}}$ b) $\dfrac{\sqrt{6}}{\sqrt{54}}$ c) $\dfrac{\sqrt{252}}{\sqrt{7}}$ d) $\dfrac{\sqrt{27x}}{\sqrt{12x^3}}$

2. Simplify.

   a) $\sqrt{\dfrac{4}{25}}$ b) $\sqrt{\dfrac{1}{9}}$ c) $-\sqrt{\dfrac{36}{121}}$

   d) $\sqrt{\dfrac{240}{2940}}$ e) $\sqrt{\dfrac{81}{25x^2}}$ f) $\sqrt{\dfrac{36y^5}{y^{15}}}$

3. Rationalize the denominator.

   a) $\sqrt{\dfrac{3}{2}}$ b) $\sqrt{\dfrac{5}{8}}$ c) $\sqrt{\dfrac{1}{24}}$ d) $\sqrt{\dfrac{6}{x}}$

   e) $\dfrac{2}{\sqrt{3}}$ f) $\dfrac{\sqrt{50}}{\sqrt{3m}}$ g) $\dfrac{\sqrt{x^5}}{\sqrt{xy}}$ h) $\dfrac{\sqrt{54a^2b^5}}{\sqrt{27a^9b^4}}$

Teaching Notes:

- Many students have trouble with example 3.
- Encourage students to write non-perfect square numbers as the product of the largest possible perfect square and another number.
- Refer students to the **Quotient Rule for Radicals** box in the textbook.
- Some students need to see several examples of how $\sqrt{a} \cdot \sqrt{a} = a$ before applying it to rationalizing a denominator.

Answers: 1a) $\dfrac{2}{3}$, b) $\dfrac{1}{3}$, c) 6, d) $\dfrac{3}{2x}$;   2a) $\dfrac{2}{5}$, b) $\dfrac{1}{3}$, c) $-\dfrac{6}{11}$, d) $\dfrac{2}{7}$, e) $\dfrac{9}{5x}$, f) $\dfrac{6}{y^5}$;   3a) $\dfrac{\sqrt{6}}{2}$, b) $\dfrac{\sqrt{10}}{4}$,

c) $\dfrac{\sqrt{6}}{12}$, d) $\dfrac{\sqrt{6x}}{x}$, e) $\dfrac{2\sqrt{3}}{3}$, f) $\dfrac{5\sqrt{6m}}{3m}$, g) $\dfrac{x^2\sqrt{y}}{y}$, h) $\dfrac{\sqrt{2ab}}{a^4}$

Addition, Subtraction, and More Multiplication

Learning Objectives:

    a   Add or subtract with radical notation, using the distributive laws to simplify.
    b   Multiply expressions involving radicals, where some of the expressions contain more than one term.
    c   Rationalize denominators having two terms.

Examples:

1. Add or subtract. Simplify by collecting like radical terms, if possible.

    a) $3\sqrt{7}+2\sqrt{7}-\sqrt{7}$ b) $\sqrt{x}-3\sqrt{x}$ c) $\sqrt{12}+\sqrt{27}$

    d) $\sqrt{50}-6\sqrt{98}+8\sqrt{72}$ e) $9\sqrt{5y}-2\sqrt{20y}$ f) $6x\sqrt{50x}-4\sqrt{18x^3}$

    g) $5\sqrt{3}+2\sqrt{\dfrac{1}{3}}$ h) $\sqrt{4x+8}+\sqrt{36x^3+72x^2}$ i) $\sqrt{\dfrac{2}{5}}-\sqrt{\dfrac{1}{10}}$

2. Multiply.

    a) $\sqrt{5}\left(\sqrt{3}+\sqrt{7}\right)$ b) $\sqrt{6}\left(4\sqrt{12}-3\sqrt{3}\right)$ c) $\left(2\sqrt{5}+\sqrt{3}\right)\left(\sqrt{5}+\sqrt{3}\right)$

    d) $\left(2\sqrt{2}+5\sqrt{10}\right)\left(2\sqrt{2}-\sqrt{10}\right)$ e) $\left(3\sqrt{5}-2\right)^2$ f) $\left(4\sqrt{3}+6\sqrt{5}\right)^2$

    g) $\left(2a\sqrt{3}-3\sqrt{2}\right)\left(2a\sqrt{3}+3\sqrt{2}\right)$ h) $\left(\sqrt{x}+3\right)^2$

3. Rationalize the denominator.

    a) $\dfrac{3}{\sqrt{3}+1}$ b) $\dfrac{7}{\sqrt{13}-\sqrt{6}}$ c) $\dfrac{2-\sqrt{8}}{5+\sqrt{8}}$

    d) $\dfrac{3}{5-\sqrt{x}}$ e) $\dfrac{3+\sqrt{x}}{\sqrt{x}-3}$ f) $\dfrac{4-\sqrt{2}}{\sqrt{x}+\sqrt{y}}$

Teaching Notes:

- Most students find example 1 easy once they realize that adding/subtracting like radicals is analogous to adding/subtracting like terms.
- Many students have trouble at first with example 2, where the square root has a coefficient other than 1 before simplification.
- Many students distribute the exponent in examples 3c) and d) instead of multiplying the binomial by itself.

Answers: 1a) $4\sqrt{7}$, b) $-2\sqrt{x}$, c) $5\sqrt{3}$, d) $11\sqrt{2}$, e) $5\sqrt{5y}$, f) $18x\sqrt{2x}$, g) $\dfrac{17\sqrt{3}}{3}$, h) $(2+6x)\sqrt{x+2}$,

i) $\dfrac{\sqrt{10}}{10}$; 2a) $\sqrt{15}+\sqrt{35}$, b) $15\sqrt{2}$, c) $13+3\sqrt{15}$, d) $-42+16\sqrt{5}$, e) $49-12\sqrt{5}$, f) $228+48\sqrt{15}$,

g) $12a^2-18$, h) $x+6\sqrt{x}+9$; 3a) $\dfrac{3\sqrt{3}-3}{2}$, b) $\sqrt{13}+\sqrt{6}$, c) $\dfrac{18-14\sqrt{2}}{17}$, d) $\dfrac{15+3\sqrt{x}}{25-x}$, e) $\dfrac{x+6\sqrt{x}+9}{x-9}$,

f) $\dfrac{4\sqrt{x}-4\sqrt{y}-\sqrt{2x}+\sqrt{2y}}{x-y}$

Radical Equations

Learning Objectives:

   a   Solve radical equations with one or two radical terms isolated, using the principle of squaring once.
   b   Solve radical equations with two radical terms, using the principle of squaring twice.
   c   Solve applied problems using radical equations.

Examples:

1.   Solve for the variable. Check your solutions.

   a) $\sqrt{x} = 7$ b) $\sqrt{y+3} = 6$ c) $\sqrt{10x-9} = 9$

   d) $\sqrt{8x-2} = \sqrt{x+4}$ e) $\sqrt{5x} - 3 = 7$ f) $\sqrt{5x-6} = x$

   g) $\sqrt{y+9} = y+3$ h) $\sqrt{x^2+4} - x + 2 = 0$ i) $\sqrt{(2x+1)(4x-5)} = x+4$

2.   Solve. Use the principle of squaring twice.

   a) $\sqrt{x+3} = \sqrt{x+21}$ b) $\sqrt{4x+1} - 1 = \sqrt{2x}$

3.   The equation $D = \sqrt{2h}$ can be used to approximate the distance D, in miles, that a person can see to the horizon from a height h, in feet.
   a) How far can a person see to the horizon from a height of 100 ft? Round to the nearest mile.
   b) Jay can see 250 mi to the horizon from an airplane. How high is the plane?

Teaching Notes:

   •   Many students find examples 1d) through i) and example 2 difficult.
   •   Show students a simple example of a possible solution which does not check, such as:
       $x = 3$ → square both sides → $x^2 = 9$ → $x = \pm 3$ → $x = -3$ does not check

Answers: _1a) 49, b) 33, c) 9, d)_ $\dfrac{6}{7}$, _e) 20, f) 2, 3, g) 0, h) no solution, i) −1, 3 ; 2a) 4, b) 0, 2; 3a) 14 mi,_

_b) 31,250 ft_

Applications with Right Triangles

Learning Objectives:

    a   Given the lengths of any two sides of a right triangle, find the length of the third side.
    b   Solve applied problems involving right triangles.

Examples:

1. A right triangle has legs a and b and hypotenuse c. Find the length of the missing side. Where appropriate, give both an exact answer and an approximation to three decimal places.

    a) $a = 2$, $b = 3$. Find c.   b) $a = \sqrt{3}$, $b = \sqrt{5}$. Find c.

    c) $a = 9$, $c = 15$. Find b.   d) $b = \sqrt{3}$, $c = \sqrt{8}$. Find a.

2. A 30-ft ladder is leaning up against a building. The bottom of the ladder is 8 ft from the building. How high is the top of the ladder?

3. Find the length of the diagonal of a square whose sides are 5 m long.

Teaching Notes:

- Some students are confused by finding a missing leg in 1c) and d).
- Encourage students to draw and label a diagram for the applied problems.

Answers: 1a) $\sqrt{13} \approx 3.606$, b) $\sqrt{8} = 2\sqrt{2} \approx 2.828$, c) 12, d) $\sqrt{5} \approx 2.236$; 2) $\sqrt{836}$ ft ≈ 28.914 ft ;
3) $\sqrt{50}$ m ≈ 7.071 m

Introduction to Quadratic Equations

Learning Objectives:

   a   Write a quadratic equation in standard form $ax^2 + bx + c = 0$, $a > 0$, and determine the coefficients a, b, and c.

   b   Solve quadratic equations of the type $ax^2 + bx = 0$, where $b \neq 0$, by factoring.

   c   Solve quadratic equations of the type $ax^2 + bx + c = 0$, where $b \neq 0$ and $c \neq 0$, by factoring.

   d   Solve applied problems involving quadratic equations.

Examples:

1. Write in standard form and determine a, b, and c.

    a) $x^2 - 4x + 3 = 0$ b) $5x^2 = 2x - 6$ c) $8 = -3x^2 + x$ d) $x^2 - 1 = x + 2$

2. Solve.

    a) $x^2 + 7x = 0$ b) $25x^2 - 5x = 0$ c) $3x^2 = 27x$ d) $8y^2 - 5y = 6y^2 - 3y$

3. Solve.

    a) $x^2 - 3x - 10 = 0$ b) $x^2 + 20 + 9x = 0$ c) $x^2 - 12x = -36$

    d) $(4x - 1)(x + 2) = 3(4x - 1)$ e) $6x^2 - 25x + 25 = 0$ f) $\dfrac{3}{x-2} + \dfrac{3}{x+2} = 2$

4. A polygon has 20 diagonals. How many sides does it have? Use $d = \dfrac{n^2 - 3n}{2}$.

Teaching Notes:

*   In example 2c), many students attempt to divide both sides by x.

Answers: 1a) $x^2 - 4x + 3 = 0$, $a = 1$, $b = -4$, $c = 3$, b) $5x^2 - 2x + 6 = 0$, $a = 5$, $b = -2$, $c = 6$, c) $3x^2 - x + 8 = 0$, $a = 3$, $b = -1$, $c = 8$, d) $x^2 - x - 3 = 0$, $a = 1$, $b = -1$, $c = -3$; 2a) 0, -7, b) 0, $\dfrac{1}{5}$, c) 0, 9, d) 0, 1; 3a) -2, 5, b) -5, -4, c) 6, d) $\dfrac{1}{4}$, 1, e) $\dfrac{5}{2}$, $\dfrac{5}{3}$, f) -1, 4; 4) 8 sides

Solving Quadratic Equations by Completing the Square

Learning Objectives:

    a   Solve quadratic equations of the type $ax^2 = p$.

    b   Solve quadratic equations of the type $(x+c)^2 = d$.

    c   Solve quadratic equations by completing the square.

    d   Solve certain applied problems involving quadratic equations of the type $ax^2 = p$.

Examples:

1. Solve.

    a) $x^2 = 9$ b) $x^2 = 20$ c) $x^2 - 75 = 0$

    d) $4x^2 = 16$ e) $3x^2 + 4 = 64$

2. Solve.

    a) $(x-5)^2 = 25$ b) $(x+3)^2 = 11$ c) $(m+3)^2 = \dfrac{3}{4}$

    d) $\left(y - \dfrac{2}{3}\right)^2 = 4$ e) $x^2 + 2x + 1 = 16$ f) $x^2 - 10x + 25 = 7$

3. Solve by completing the square.

    a) $x^2 + 4x = -3$ b) $x^2 - 2x - 35 = 0$ c) $x^2 + 18x + 67 = 0$

    d) $2x^2 - 5x = 3$ e) $q^2 + 3q - 1 = 0$ f) $d^2 - 6d + 2 = -5$

4. A ball is dropped from a building 200 ft tall. The equation $d = 16t^2$ gives the distance the ball falls after t seconds. How long will it take for the ball to hit the ground? Round to the nearest tenth of a second.

Teaching Notes:

- Many students forget to include the $\pm$ when using the principle of square roots.
- Most students are confused by completing the square at first and need to see many examples of how to figure out what number must be added to complete the square.
- Refer students to the **Solving by Completing the Square** box in the textbook.

Answers: *1a)* $-3, 3$, *b)* $-2\sqrt{5}, 2\sqrt{5}$, *c)* $-5\sqrt{3}, 5\sqrt{3}$, *d)* $-2, 2$, *e)* $-2\sqrt{5}, 2\sqrt{5}$; *2a)* $0, 10$, *b)* $-3 \pm \sqrt{11}$,

c) $\dfrac{-6 \pm \sqrt{3}}{2}$, *d)* $-\dfrac{4}{3}, \dfrac{8}{3}$, *e)* $-5, 3$, *f)* $5 \pm \sqrt{7}$; *3a)* $-3, -1$, *b)* $-5, 7$, *c)* $-9 \pm \sqrt{14}$, *d)* $-\dfrac{1}{2}, 3$,

e) $\dfrac{-3 \pm \sqrt{13}}{2}$, *f)* $3 \pm \sqrt{2}$; *4)* 3.5 sec

The Quadratic Formula

Learning Objectives:

    a   Solve quadratic equations using the quadratic formula.
    b   Find approximate solutions of quadratic equations using a calculator.

Examples:

1. Solve. Try factoring first. If factoring is not possible or is difficult, use the quadratic formula.

    a) $x^2 + 5x + 6 = 0$ b) $x^2 + 4x - 7 = 0$ c) $3x^2 - 9x = -2$

    d) $3x^2 - 4x + 8 = 0$ e) $5x^2 = -10x - 3$ f) $x^2 + \dfrac{4}{5}x = -\dfrac{1}{5}$

    g) $9x^2 - 6x + 1 = 0$ h) $25x^2 + 20x + 4 = 0$ i) $8x^2 - 15x - 2 = 0$

    j) $3x^2 + 10x = -6$ k) $x - 4 = \dfrac{3}{x-4}$ l) $\dfrac{1}{x} + \dfrac{1}{x+5} = \dfrac{1}{2}$

2. Solve using the quadratic formula. Use a calculator to approximate the solutions to the nearest tenth.

    a) $4x^2 + 6x + 1 = 0$ b) $x^2 + 4x = 6$ c) $x^2 + x - 22 = 0$

    d) $x^2 + x - 3 = 0$ e) $3x^2 = -16x + 100$ f) $2x^2 + 5x = -1$

Teaching Notes:

- Remind students to put the equation in standard form before identifying a, b, and c.
- Many students simplify final answers incorrectly. For example, they incorrectly simplify:
  $$\frac{4 \pm \sqrt{5}}{8} \rightarrow \frac{1 \pm \sqrt{5}}{2}.$$
- Some students prefer to always use the quadratic formula because it has no restrictions on when it can be used. Encourage them to also master the other methods, which are often quicker and easier to apply.

Answers: *1a)* -3, -2, *b)* $-2 \pm \sqrt{11}$, *c)* $\dfrac{9 \pm \sqrt{57}}{6}$, *d) no real-number solutions, e)* $\dfrac{-5 - \sqrt{10}}{5}$, $\dfrac{-5 + \sqrt{10}}{5}$,

f) no real-number solutions, g) $\dfrac{1}{3}$, *h)* $-\dfrac{2}{5}$, *i)* $-\dfrac{1}{8}$, 2, *j)* $\dfrac{-5 \pm \sqrt{7}}{3}$, *k)* $4 \pm \sqrt{3}$, *l)* $\dfrac{-1 \pm \sqrt{41}}{2}$;

2a) -1.3, -0.2, *b)* -5.2, 1.2, *c)* -5.2, 4.2, *d)* -2.3, 1.3, *e)* -9.0, 3.7, *f)* -2.3, -0.2

Formulas

Learning Objective:

a   Solve a formula for a specified letter.

Examples:

Solve. Assume letters represent nonnegative numbers.

1. Solve for x: $k = \dfrac{m}{x}$.

2. Solve for y: $a = \dfrac{5t}{y^2}$.

3. Solve for d: $\dfrac{1}{a} + \dfrac{1}{d} = \dfrac{1}{t}$.

4. Solve for m: $A = 3(m+n)$.

5. Solve for z: $G = \sqrt{\dfrac{2z}{y}}$.

6. Solve for x: $D = mx^2 + nx + p$.

7. Solve for d: $M = \dfrac{c-d}{3d}$.

8. Solve for p: $\dfrac{t}{p} = \dfrac{q}{s}$.

Teaching Note:

- It is helpful to ask students to identify the type of equation they have before they attempt to solve for the letter.

Answers: *1)* $x = \dfrac{m}{k}$; *2)* $y = \pm\sqrt{\dfrac{5t}{a}}$; *3)* $d = \dfrac{at}{a-t}$; *4)* $m = \dfrac{A-3n}{3}$; *5)* $z = \dfrac{G^2 y}{2}$;

6) $x = \dfrac{-n + \sqrt{n^2 - 4mp}}{2m}$; *7)* $d = \dfrac{c}{1+3M}$; *8)* $p = \dfrac{st}{q}$

Applications and Problem Solving

Learning Objective:

a   Solve applied problems using quadratic equations.

Examples:

Solve.

1. The area of a rectangular garden is 84 ft^2. The length is 2 ft longer than twice the width. Find the dimensions of the garden.

2. The hypotenuse of a right triangle is 10 cm long. One leg is 3 cm longer than the other leg. Find the lengths of the legs to the nearest tenth.

3. The length of a rectangle is 3 times its width. The area is 60 in^2. Find the dimensions. Round to the nearest tenth.

4. A picture frame measures 25 cm by 35 cm. There is 651 cm^2 of picture showing. The frame is of uniform width. How wide is the frame?

5. The speed of a boat in still water is 12 km/h. The boat travels 45 km upstream and 45 km downstream in a total time of 8 hr. What is the speed of the current in the stream?

Teaching Notes:

- Many students find this section difficult.
- Most students benefit by setting up a chart to solve distance and work problems.
- Encourage students to draw and label a diagram and to list any relevant formulas whenever possible.

Answers: *1) length = 14 ft, width = 6 ft; 2) 5.4 cm, 8.4 cm; 3) length = 13.4 in., width = 4.5 in.; 4) 2 cm; 5) 3km/h*

Graphs of Quadratic Equations

Learning Objectives:

    a   Graph quadratic equations.
    b   Find the x-intercepts of a quadratic equation.

Examples:

1. Find five ordered pairs for the equation. Then graph it.

    a) $y = x^2 + 1$ b) $y = x^2 - 2$ c) $y = \dfrac{1}{2}x^2$ d) $y = -\dfrac{1}{4}x^2$

    e) $y = -2x^2 + 2$ f) $y = (x+3)^2$ g) $y = (x-2)^2$ h) $y = \dfrac{1}{4}(x+1)^2$

2. Determine the vertex and the x-intercepts. Then sketch the graph.

    a) $y = x^2 - 1$ b) $y = x^2 + 4x$ c) $y = x^2 + 2x - 3$

    d) $y = -x^2 + 2x + 3$ e) $y = x^2 + 5x + 4$

Teaching Notes:

- Many students need to be told at first what x values to use when finding ordered pairs.
- Remind students that if their ordered pairs do not make the approximate vertex position apparent when graphing, then more ordered pairs are needed.
- Most students are comfortable using the vertex formula, but some are confused at first by why the calculated value must be put back into the quadratic equation.
- Encourage students to also graph the y-intercepts in example 2.

Answers: 1) see graph answer pages; 2a) vertex (0,–1), x–int (1,0), (–1,0), b) vertex (–2,–4), x–int (–4,0), (0,0), c) vertex (–1,–4), x–int (–3,0), (1,0), d) vertex (1,4), x–int(–1,0), (3,0), e) vertex (–5/2,–9/4), x–int (–4,0), (–1,0), see graph answer pages

Functions

Learning Objectives:

    a   Determine whether a correspondence is a function.
    b   Given a function described by an equation, find function values (outputs) for specified values (inputs).
    c   Draw a graph of a function.
    d   Determine whether a graph is that of a function.
    e   Solve applied problems involving functions and their graphs.

Examples:

1. Determine whether each correspondence is a function.

    a)

        $1 \longrightarrow 3$
        $2 \longrightarrow 5$
        $4 \longrightarrow 1$

    b)

      $-1 \searrow$
      $1 \longrightarrow 3$
      $2 \longrightarrow -5$

    c)

      $7 \longrightarrow -1$
        $\searrow 4$
      $3 \longrightarrow 5$

2. For each function, find the indicated function value.

    a) $f(x) = -2x + 6;\ f(-1)$ b) $f(x) = 3x^2 + x - 5;\ f(0)$ c) $f(x) = 2|x| - 1;\ f(-3)$

3. Complete the table for the function defined by $f(x) = x - 3$. Then graph the function.

	x	$x - 3$	$f(x)$
a	-3		
b	-2		
c	-1		
d	0		
e	1		

4. Decide whether each relation represents a function.

    a)

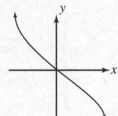

    b)

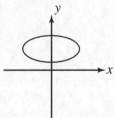

Teaching Notes:

- Students find this section easy.
- Have students name different real-world relationships which represent functions.
- One way of viewing a function is to think of it as a box with an input and an output and a crank which takes in an input and produces an output.

Mini-Lecture 2.7:

2a)

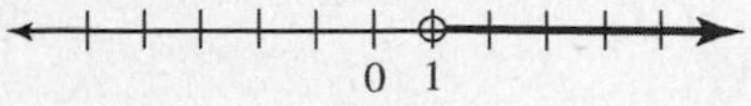

b)

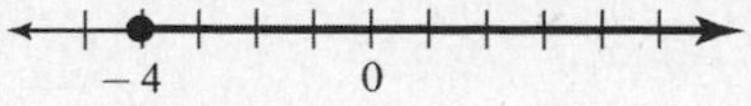

c)

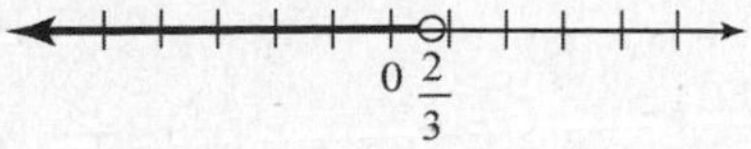

d)

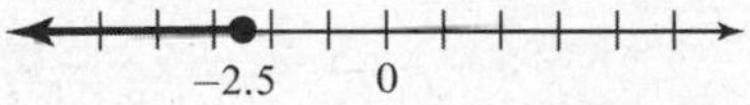

e)

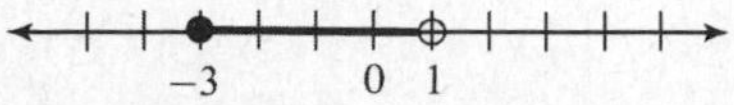

Mini-Lecture 3.1:

1a–g)

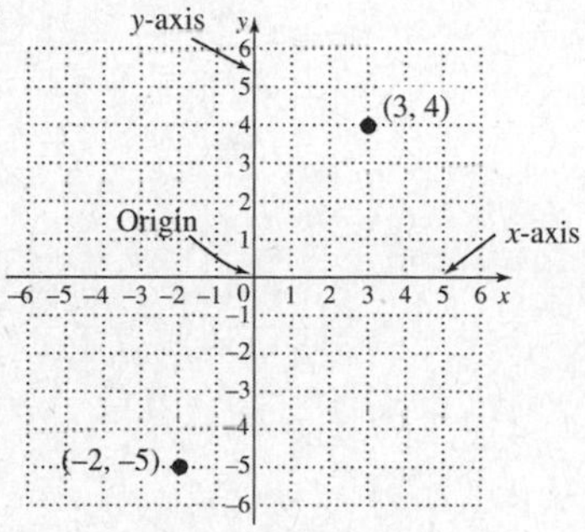

3a)

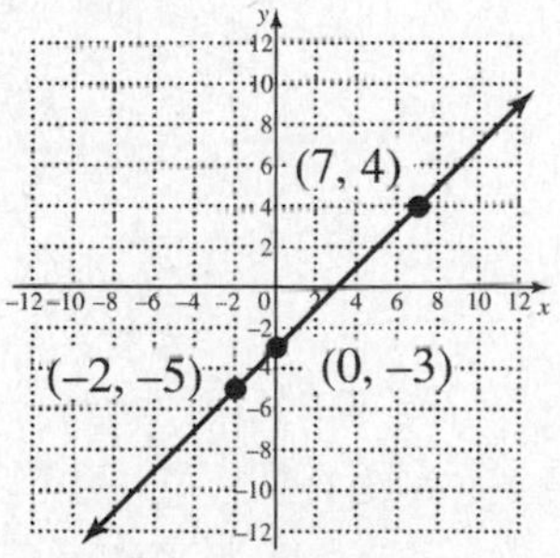

b)

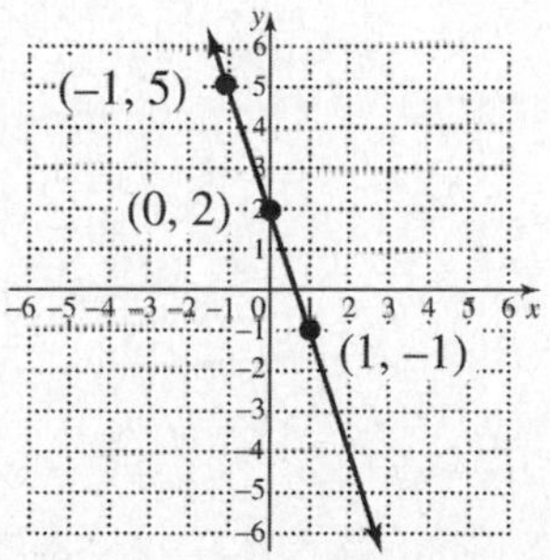

c)

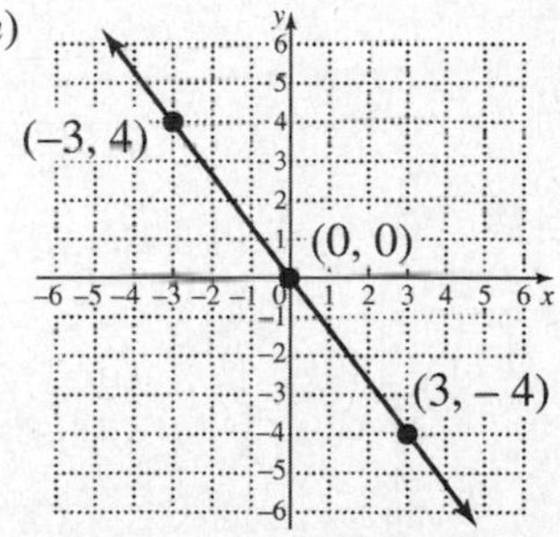

4a) $(0,4)$

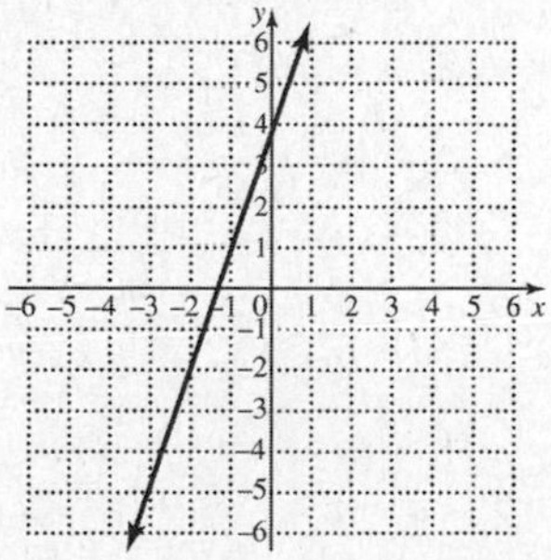

b) $(0,2)$

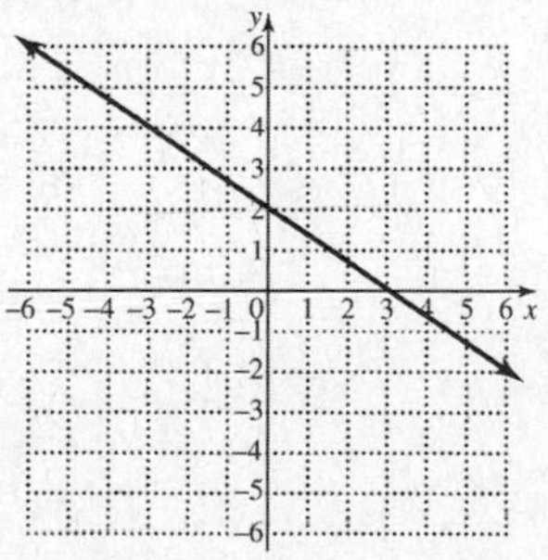

c) $(0,4)$

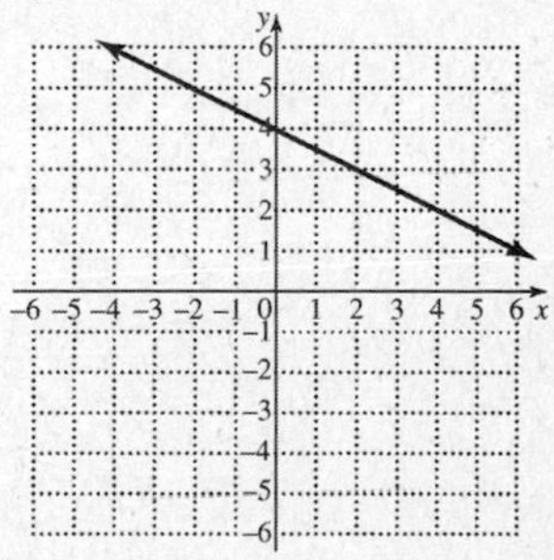

d) $(0, 3)$

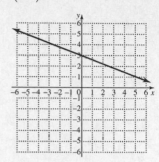

5a)

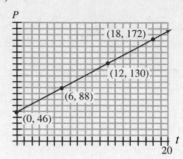

Mini-Lecture 3.2:

2a)

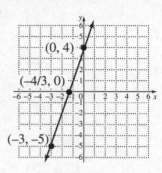

b)

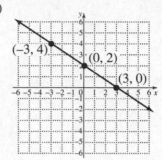

c)

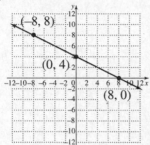

d)

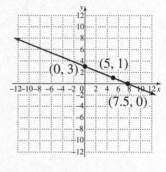

3a)

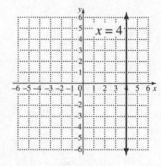

b)

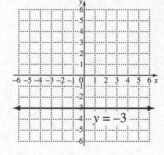

c)

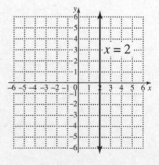

d)

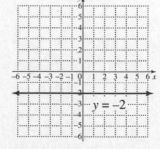

Mini-Lecture 3.5

2a)
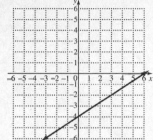

b)
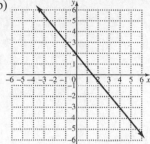

c)
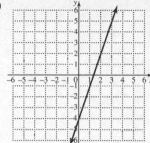

d)
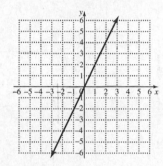

Mini-Lecture 3.7

2a)
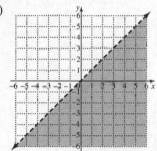

b)
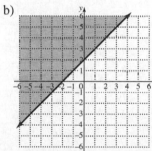

c)
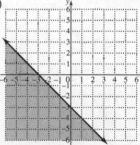

d)
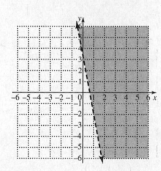

e)
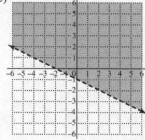

f)
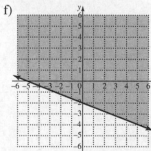

g)
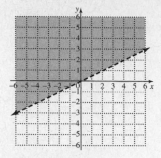

h)
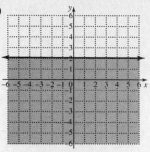

i)
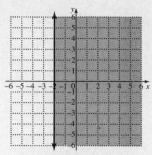

j)
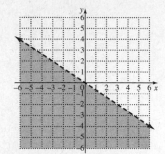

k)
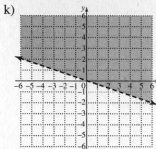

l)
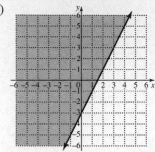

Mini-Lecture 7.1

2a)
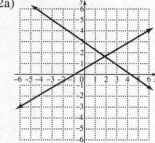

b)
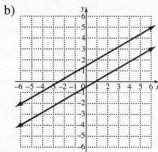

c)
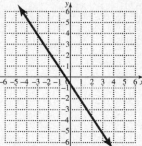

3a)
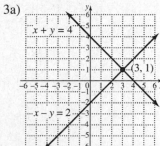

b)
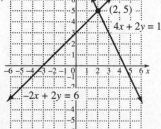

c)

4a)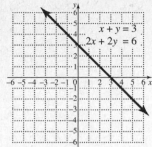

b)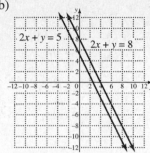

c)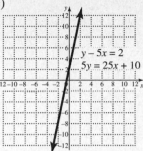

d)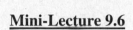

Mini-Lecture 9.6

1a)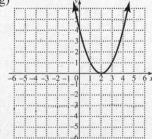

b)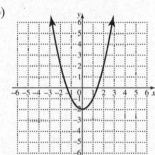

c)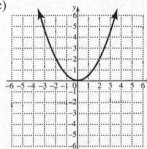

d)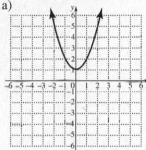

e)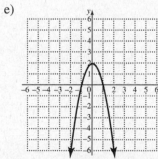

f)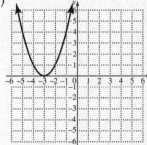

g)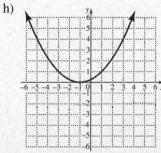

h)

2a)
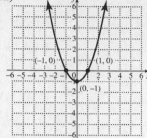

b)
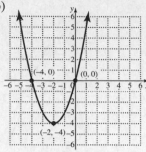

c)
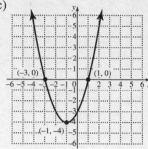

d)
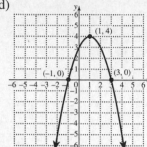

e)
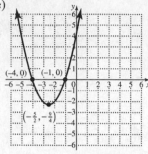

Mini-Lecture 9.7

2a)
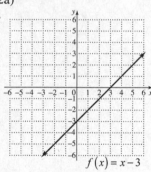

$f(x) = x - 3$

GENERAL, FIRST-TIME ADVICE

We asked the contributing professors for words of advice to instructors who are teaching this course for the first time or for the first time in a long while. Their responses can be found on the following pages.

Endre Borsos, *Miami-Dade Community College*

When I first started teaching I introduced myself to the class as a first-time teacher. This should never be done by a rookie. Introduction is important but the level of details (first-time teacher) should be avoided.

Gail G. Burkett, *Palm Beach Community College*

Before you begin the Semester:

1. Be sure that your syllabus is detailed and adhere to it. If you make an exception for one, you have to be fair and do it for all. It is imperative to be fair. Be sure to have a written cell phone policy. I am pretty strict about cell phones, so my rule is that if a second phone goes off during a class, then everyone gets a pop quiz. If it goes off during a test, the offender gets five points off the test. In 5 years, I've only had to implement this three or four times.

2. Ask the department chair about the reliability of the standardized placement tests used to place students in the class. I use a diagnostic quiz on day one that contains the prerequisite skills needed for the course. The students who do poorly on it are then instructed to spend time in the math lab, 4–6 hours a week until the first test to remediate their basic skills.

3. If you are unsure of any of the course objectives, ask one of the 'seasoned' instructors.

4. At the beginning of the first class meeting, I have students introduce themselves to at least two other students sitting near them. I instruct them to share their college goal with each other. This really helps the nervous, first time college students and builds rapport in the classroom.

5. Adhere to your schedule as much as possible. It is your job to make sure all of the required material is covered.

6. Hand out practice tests. I usually have 40–50 questions on them, and then whittle it down to 20 or 25 for the test. This gets students familiar with the directions and can greatly reduce test anxiety. If students tell you they are just bad at taking tests, tell them to do the practice test 10 times!

7. I make up three or more versions of the test so I don't have to worry too much about cheating. Do watch out for notes on the baseball cap bill (inside), notes on the inside of the calculator cover and notes on the floor (the study sheet left on top of their books). Remember cell phones can have pictures of notes and friends can text message information.

8. Be strict on your make-up policy and no retests! I have heard incredible stories (complete with tears!) that turned out be a ruse to get out of the test they weren't ready to take. Part of our job is to get students ready for the business world. Do you think a boss wants to hear why they didn't make the deadline? To compensate for the no make-up policy, I drop their lowest grade if it is to their advantage. I've also had a policy where their final would count double if they miss a test.

9. Return tests at the end of the next class. It's also wise to have them correct their mistakes (I give extra credit on the subsequent test for this) unless you give multiple choice questions.

10. I have found that checking homework 'daily', although inconvenient, helps to solve the 'terminal procrastination syndrome' of many 'just out of high schoolers'. It helps build good study skills.

General Teaching Advice:

1. When you're covering examples in the objectives, cover each one thoroughly. Quality is more important than quantity. Don't use the same examples as the text; students can look at those on their own! Have your problems ready ahead of time and make sure you've tried them before class! It can be embarrassing and disastrous to be halfway through a problem and find it has unsuspected kinks!

2. Students have different learning styles and it's important to address them all. Not many developmental students find a traditional lecture for the entire class very beneficial. I show them an example. Then I have them try one with me. Then I have them try one on their own or with their neighbor. Verbalizing the procedures can be a very helpful process.

3. Math anxiety is real for many of our students. One way to help overcome anxiety is confidence. Doing the practice test repeatedly, under testing conditions, until they are certain about how to do each problem correctly, can help deter the jitters.

4. I've had students say they understand the material when they are in class, but go blank during a test. I explain that it may be because they don't really know it, they just think they do. An analogy is that I can watch a chef make a soufflé and understand each step but that doesn't mean I can do it myself! For these students, I suggest they try 'teaching' the problems to a family member or friend. They definitely know the material if they can teach it!

5. When you're at the board, try to face the students as much as possible. It is very difficult to understand someone with their back to you, talking to the wall! Keep your board work organized. Also, it's a good habit if you let them know when you are moving on to new material. They can keep their notes more organized and know a transition is coming.

6. I admit I can make mistakes and the person that catches me gets an extra credit point. That keeps it positive!

7. On important objectives, I ask the students to give me a 'thumbs up' if they understand it before I move on. If I don't get enough facing up, I try a few more examples and ask for questions.

8. Begin each class with questions on the previous homework. This provides a review and a chance for the stragglers to get in before the new material is presented.

Bill Graesser, *Ivy Tech State College*

1. What I have learned over time is something that we all realize but sometimes forget. We all have a different style of learning. We present material and sometimes expect students to just pick it up the first time around. It is not always that simple. One approach may work for one student, but not another. Take your time. Be patient. You can't assume that just because you went over something, everyone will remember it three weeks later. Don't be afraid to put in review problems from material two or three weeks old. Don't be upset if students don't remember it even if you have gone over it three or four times. Practice is still the key to successful math skills.

2. Another thing I believe is that giving lots of homework (50–60 problems) each night does not necessarily help all students retain a process for doing different problems. Selecting 10 or 15 specific problems can accomplish the same goal. From those original 10 or 15, you can assign 3 or 4 more each week in review and accomplish the same goal. In being selective with the problems, be sure to pick problems that challenge the students. Pick problems that allow students to think about what they are doing. In addition, pick at least one or two problems that cannot be done or simply contradict the main rules. Pick problems that allow them to practice the rules and also apply them to a more real world application.

Rosa Kavanaugh, *Ozarks Technical College*

1. Mathematical language and notation are foreign and confusing for students who are seeing algebra for the first time. Much of the mathematical language has meaning in the more familiar English language. Although developmental mathematics students also have weak language skills, we can help them identify words by associating them with the English language. These associations can help our students make the connections that will give the mathematical language more meaning to them. A good example is the word "distribute." This is a good time to encourage some discussion of the meaning of the word in common everyday language and then make the connections to the specific mathematical meaning.

2. Perhaps the most troublesome counterexample to the notion that mathematical language has meaning in the English language is in the words "term" and "factor." In the English language, these words do not have the same specific meaning that they do in mathematics. When we say, "These were factors in our decision," that does not mean that those "factors" were multiplied. When we say, "These were the terms of our agreement." that does not mean that the "terms" were added. Yet these same words have those very precise meaning in mathematics.

In the English language we use the word "term" in a very generic way. The word "term" should be used very deliberately and precisely in the mathematics classroom.

3. In some cases, it may be helpful to point out and relate the root words. For example, when I first write the word "evaluate" on the board, I underline the letters valu. I explain to the students that when they see this word, these letters can help them remember that they are being asked to "find the value." Underlining the word <u>ratio</u> in the word <u>ratio</u>nal, helps students to connect <u>ratio</u>nal numbers to fractions.

4. Students often confuse problem types on exams. One reason is that they tend to overlook the instructions as they do homework since all of the problems in a section tend to be the same type. I believe that the instructor should not only emphasize the meaning of the instructions but also write the instructions as part of the example. Students in developmental mathematics classes tend to include in their notes much of what is written on the board, but little of the words that the instructor says, but does not write. Thus it is important that the instructor not only say, "Solve" but also write:

   "Solve $3x + 5 = 5(x - 1)$ "

   This kind of emphasis helps students avoid common confusion such as the difference between "Solve" and "Simplify."

   After presenting examples of both types, the instructor can write on the board:

   Solve $3x + 5 = 5(x - 1)$

   and

   Simplify $3x + 5 - 5(x - 1)$.

   Then the instructor could ask: "What is the difference between these two problems and how would you know the difference if you saw both of them on an exam?" This tends to encourage students to do some critical thinking and develop a better understanding of the processes involved.

5. Mathematics instructors themselves must model good mathematical notation. One of my notation "pet peeves" is improper use of equals signs. Occasionally adjunct faculty insert errant equal signs as they perform intermediate steps of a problem.

6. Another more subtle but, I believe, equally serious error is the omission of equals signs between simplification steps. Perhaps one of the most common occurrences of this is in the demonstration of the factoring process. For example, I observe a number of faculty who write a factoring problem as:

$$3x^4 - 12y^4$$
$$3(x^4 - 4y^4)$$
$$3(x^2 + 2y^2)(x^2 - 2y^2)$$

Omitting the equals signs between the steps is not only mathematically unsound but also eliminates the rationale for checking the result of a factoring problem by redistributing because they should be **equal**.

7. Correct mathematical language can also be an issue. Some instructors say "LCM" when they mean "LCD." Another common error is confusion of "expression" and "equation." If we are to convince our student that mathematics is a precise discipline with precise language, our own language must also model such precision.

8. Instructors should be prepared not only to describe to students what the process is but also to explain **why** the process works. This may not be an issue for some students but is particularly important to many adult learners. They may have heard the rules before but did not buy into the validity of the process. This stumbling block is sometimes an impediment to further learning in the course. Instructors need to be willing to provide such explanations during class if time permits. For example, some students never saw the validity of the rules for operations with signed numbers. Others are still confused about **why** division by zero is undefined. Settling these kinds of questions allows students to progress in topics where they were confused in the past.

9. The text contains a good introduction to the benefits of students' recognizing and using the learning objectives of each section. One other use of these objectives that we recommend to students is in preparing for exams. So many students at this level have never learned how to study. They tend to believe that the way to prepare for an exam is to work all of the several hundred problems assigned for homework. We find Bittinger's a, b, c,... coding of learning objectives very helpful in convincing students that they do not have to rework all of the problems in a given section but should instead concentrate on one from each objective to identify their areas of strength and weakness. Then they understand that if they have difficulty, they can return to the discussion correlating to that objective in the section/chapter.

Deloria Nanze-Davis, *Texas Southmost College and University of Texas-Brownsville*

The teaching tips listed below will help students learn terminology, concepts and problem solving techniques more quickly.

1. Always use correct terminology.
2. Quiz students on definitions and terms.
3. Have students go to the board to work and explain problems to their classmates.
4. Have students work in groups when it comes to solving algebraic word problems.
5. Always assign homework
6. Assign as many word problems as possible.
7. Assign the synthesis problems.
8. Encourage the students to read the lesson before coming to class.

Jane Duncan Nesbit, *Columbia Union College*

1. Be aware of the diversity of students in regards to ability. Some believe they were misplaced into this remedial class (and already know all this stuff) and others really need a thorough review of arithmetic and/or algebra. Use cooperative learning to get the smart ones to help those who are struggling.
2. Many students are scared of mathematics. Address this issue the first day and allow them to journal their fears to you as the instructor. I have always used the analogy of becoming a great basketball star. I ask them "can I become a great basketball player by watching Michael Jordan?" NO, I must practice dribbling, shooting, blocking, passing, etc. The same idea applies to mathematics—you cannot just watch the teacher practice, but you must practice until you master the material yourself. MATH IS NOT A SPECTATOR SPORT.
3. I wouldn't allow a calculator until Chapter 2 to make sure the students are able to perform arithmetic operations by hand.
4. Train students to be disciplined and thorough in doing their work.

Louise Olshan, *County College of Morris*

1. I think it is important to remember that in a remedial course, I am doing much more than just teaching the content of the course. I try to teach study

skills, time management, the need to use all the resources available, such as my Office Hours, the tutoring offered by the Math Center and the extensive materials available from MyMathLab. It is important for students to know that getting extra help is not a sign of failure, but a sign of maturity—recognizing that more needs to be done on their part to learn what is not understood at the time.

2. It is important for me to have a positive attitude and to encourage my students. Many have encountered algebra in high school and have struggled with the material.
3. Many of my students think that algebra is "a bunch of rules" that don't make sense, but rather need to be memorized. I try to minimize the memorization and maximize the understanding of the steps needed in a problem. I stress the logic and beauty of the mathematics.
4. Students need to be active in class. Having worksheets for class and having students work on them as I walk around tells me what I need to re-teach or that it is okay to move ahead. This method also provides me with time to help students individually.
5. As I try to show students how they need to set aside time for study and homework, I model in class that I must stay close to the departmental syllabus. I begin class with a "to-do" list of what needs to be accomplished that day. I do not always finish the list completely, but I can never stray too far from my plans. Just as I need to keep on schedule, so too must the students keep up with assignments and class material.
6. A section is not done and forgotten when a test is handed in. Going over tests during Office Hours or at the end of a class meeting allows me to correct misconceptions as I talk with students. I learn a lot from these sessions that I can incorporate into future lectures to avoid students ending up with the wrong ideas. I also learn from these sessions what I must readdress in the present class.
7. I stay away from mentioning "wrong" ways to do things, because, for some reason, this is often what gets remembered.
8. I stress Skill Maintenance so that material is not easily forgotten. Beginning class with a problem "from the past" is a good way to keep the material fresh. Students can work on this problem while I am taking roll. I go over the solution quickly and help students at the end of class, if they need further explanation.

9. The motto for my classes is "Keep It Simple". I try not to have different/special cases for students to learn.

10. It is important to always use the correct terminology and to have students speak mathematics correctly. For example, rather than saying "multiply", it is better to say "multiply both sides of the equation". Students can find their own errors sometimes by saying the step thoroughly. Also saying the step correctly can prevent errors in the first place.

Tatiana Sviridovsky, *Delaware County Community College*

The successful teaching of this course and good performance of the students depend very much on how well organized the teacher is on the first day of class. As I meet the students and introduce myself, I ask everyone to take their pencils, write down three good things about being in class and share it with the group. It's a nice icebreaker and many students choose to participate in this simple activity. I also take time on the first day to go over the following things:

1. The syllabus: Include course objectives, attendance policies, and grading procedures. Many students are disappointed by the placement into a course at this level. At DCCC the course title is "Developmental Math" and I explain to them that it's mainly Algebra, not anything very basic. It would be naïve to say that the word "Algebra" makes them very happy, but at least they don't feel like first graders. Additionally, I explain that this course opens the doors to the courses in science, business and economics. In grading, I moved away from the concept of the weighted average. I simply calculate the total number of points they accumulate during the semester.

2. The weekly schedule: I prefer all students to know when the graded work will be given to them. If you don't plan very well from the beginning, you'll never make it even to the midpoint of the course, given the amount of the material and overall level of students. I tell them that we must follow the schedule and if they have major difficulties, I am willing to spend extra time on some sections, but it must be done before or after class.

3. Prerequisites: Don't stop at just telling the students that the course has specific prerequisites. Check students' records to be sure. It's not unusual that some of them manage to register for the course when the prerequisite is not met. It's less frequent,

but possible that the student was registered for this course by mistake and the placement is actually a level or two higher.

4. MyMathLab sources: I encourage the students to use them and I show them how much this website has to offer to make their life easier.

5. The importance of the homework: The graded handouts that we complete in class are all open notes. This is my way to check the quality of the homework. These handouts account for approximately 23% of the course grade.

6. The structure of the textbook: Based on the very first section, I show the students how the material is sorted by objectives first in the part that has explanations and solved examples, then it has the same objectives in the problem set. I remind them that there is a chapter review and chapter test for each chapter and show them what the answer key includes.

7. Communications: I tell the students to highlight the portion of the syllabus that has my office location, phone number and e-mail address. I let them know that I check the email in the evening and during the weekend. I think it's important for the students to be able to get a quick response from their teacher.

8. Special accommodations: It's not enough to simply include this paragraph in the syllabus because they don't bother to read anything other than (maybe) the grading system. I always say in class that "help is available, but if you don't tell us, we don't know" to motivate the students to contact the Leaning Disabilities specialist on campus.

9. Cumulative final exam: I don't want the students to develop any anxiety from day one. I tell them that as we move through the sections, whenever there is a problem that should be put on the review list, I'll let them know. Additionally, the Student Resource Guide has a sample final with the answer key. Our department creates the actual exam based on that sample final.

10. Academic Honesty: To avoid giving the students any creative ideas, I never spend too much time explaining all possible ways of cheating in the contemporary world (such as taking the picture of the test with a camera phone). The highest numbers that I usually see in students' evaluations are for treating them with respect, and I always share this fact with my new class. I say that they are here not just to learn math, but to learn what it means to create and maintain the atmosphere of mutual trust

and respect. I try to deliver the message to them that any dishonest action in class is not just a violation of the policies; it's a demonstration of disrespect to the classmates and the teacher.

During the first class I also distribute a brief questionnaire asking students to share with me (on a voluntary basis) the information about their learning styles, strengths and weaknesses and other things that they consider to be significant in terms of their success in my course.

If you promise the students to include some bonus work into the everyday routine, it can make a real difference for them. However, I never give them false expectations that the bonus work will have an extremely high weight in the course overall grade.

Sharon Testone, *Onondaga Community College*

1. Students enrolled in an introductory algebra course at the community college level are often extremely math anxious. These students are different from those you may have taught at four-year colleges/universities or in secondary schools. They are often returning adults and need to be treated with respect and understanding. A kind word of encouragement or a smile means the world to these students. Many of these people have accomplished many things in their lives and they just have difficulty with math. Instructors should encourage all students not to feel badly about being in this course and should help them to see that their "worth" to society is not measured by their mathematical ability.

2. An important time management tip is to count the number of class periods, subtract the number of "testing days" and subtract at least two class periods for review at the end of the semester. This result is the number of instructional periods. Divide the number of instructional periods into the number of sections that need to be taught. This result gives the approximate number of sections that need to be taught each class period. This simple calculation will help new faculty avoid the pitfall of moving too quickly or too slowly through the course. Additionally, the faculty member will most likely complete all topics in the syllabus and not omit any essential material.

3. Always be on time to class and always end the class on time. Our students have very busy schedules and faculty needs to respect that fact.

4. Always be prepared for class and always hand back graded homework, quizzes, and tests the very next class period.

5. Before teaching the course for the first time, ask your department chairperson what the prerequisites are for this course. This information will assist you in gauging what knowledge the students should have when entering your classroom. They may not be completely prepared, but you will know what skills they are expected to possess and you will not spend much time reteaching material from the previous course. Additionally, determine what course(s) your students will enroll in after completing your course. Be sure that you prepare the students for those courses, but don't teach the topics from them.

6. Students at this level need to **practice, practice, practice.** Develop additional worksheets and allow time for group practice in class. Have individual students or a representative from the group show you at least one completed problem before the end of the class period. (Another alternative is to have a group representative put the solution on the board.) This technique helps to ensure that students will be able to do their homework.

7. Often students at this level do not complete their homework assignments and this leads to failure. One option is to require that students complete homework assignments in a separate notebook. On test days instructors can review the notebook (without actually grading it) to determine if students are completing their assignments. Another option is to collect homework daily or randomly and grade it.

8. Giving a 5-minute quiz after reviewing homework questions at the beginning of the class period is often helpful for new instructors. The quiz results will let both the students and the instructor know how they are doing. If the whole class fails a quiz, then most likely the instructor needs to make improvements.

9. Prepare handouts with matching overheads or Power Point slides. Students at this level are often not good note takers and have difficulty listening and writing at the same time. Handouts that include key concepts, one or two worked-out examples, and two or three problems for the students to complete immediately are very useful.

10. Have fun!! Teaching introductory algebra is *not* about the material. It is about the students. The challenge is to present the material in a way that the students can understand it and enjoy learning algebra.

11. General guidelines:
    - Set deadlines, be consistent with feedback and provide reminders if students fall behind.
    - Ask questions to determine where/why students are having difficulties.
    - Use tentative language: "It appears that you misunderstood the course requirements," instead of "Obviously, you weren't listening when I explained the requirements."
    - Put yourself in a student's place and be flexible when necessary.
    - Following the above guidelines may reduce attrition, which may be caused by several factors:
    - Lack of prerequisite skills – math, reading and/or time management
    - Lack of interaction among students, lack of interaction with instructor
    - Course pacing or impact of taking too many courses at once
    - Other responsibilities—home, family, job, etc.

Angela Walters, *Capitol College*

1. When I first taught introductory algebra, I wish I had known more about using group projects in class to help students learn the material. I find that assigning a group of 3 or 4 students a project relating to the material covered in class is an effective way for the students to learn the topic. The projects are normally about two pages in length and take no more than 20 to 30 minutes to complete. I now try to teach the course like a workshop, where the students do most of the work and I minimize the amount of talking I need to do.

2. Stress real world applications as much as possible. This way, students will understand that there is a reason that they need to learn the material.

3. It is important to collect or grade some of the homework problems to ensure that the students are doing them. I find that if the homework is not collected/graded, a majority of the students do not do the problems.

4. I find it beneficial to use verbal descriptions to tell students what I'm going to do when solving a problem and then to repeat these descriptions when I do the problem so the students learn the underlying principles and not just the technique for solving a specific problem. I will then, either in class or on an exam, ask the students to verbally describe how they would solve a particular problem.

5. I try to use concept maps or flow charts to relate the topics in a chapter. I will refer back to them frequently to remind students how the topics are related. This is also a nice method of assessment. I let the students fill in the blanks in the concept map to see how well they understand the ideas in the chapter.

Roy West, *Robeson Community College*

Remember that the material being taught is developmental. A lot of times college instructors feel that most students just need some extra practice and they will catch on. This may be true for some classes. You as an instructor need to feel them out. I personally have found that nothing replaces working problems for them in class and showing the various situations that can occur. The responsible student will get the practice they need when they do the homework problems themselves at home. Use your class time wisely.

Annette Wiesner, *University of Wisconsin-Parkside*

Don't assume that any topic is too easy. Explain everything and give at least three examples. One reason I like the Bittinger book is the review chapter at the beginning. It is important for the student to know the basics (fractions) in order to understand algebra (rational expressions).

Attendance: To save time taking attendance each day, I send around an attendance sheet. The attendance sheet is a table with students' names in the first column and blank columns for each day of the week. Students are asked to sign next to their name, under the appropriate day. At the end of each class I "highlight" the empty spots so students cannot fill in the entire week on the last day. These attendance sheets are great when counselors or coaches ask about a particular student. The Financial Aid Office often needs to know the last date a student attended a class. I also write "see me" after a student's name if I need to talk to them about something.

	Mon. 5/6	Weds. 5/8	Fri. 5/10
Jones, Harry			
Smith, Mary			

Grades: Test students on gradually increasing amounts of information and use as many sources as possible:

Daily – homework on one section

Weekly – quiz on two or three sections of the chapter
The day before the test – review in-class worksheet
Every two to three weeks – test on one or two chapters
End of the semester – final exam on entire material

Syllabus: Be sure that your syllabus clearly states assignments and due dates, test dates, tutoring center hours, how grades are determined, make-up test policy, university drop and withdraw dates, consequences for late assignments or missing tests, attendance and tardy policy, etc. You can always make an exception for a particular student with a good excuse.

Homework: I don't have time to collect and grade homework on a daily basis. I have tried three different methods to resolve this problem.

1. At the beginning of each chapter, I give a ten-point worksheet containing ten to fifteen problems. The worksheet has a "sample" of each type of problem that the student is required to know. I call this an "advanced organizer." It lets students see at a glance what the chapter is about. I assign more problems for practice, but I do not collect them. Each worksheet is worth about ten points for a total of 100 points.

2. I hand out a detailed section-by-section list of assignments. I collect the "homework packet" on the day of the test. I generally look for two or three specific problems; other than that, I grade on the completeness of the packet. I give four of these packets, worth 25 points each (or one test grade).

3. The last method I use is to give a daily assignment and specify four problems from the assignment to be handed in. I require the students to divide their paper into four squares, one problem per square. This makes it easier to grade. All assignments are due the following class period, no exceptions. I drop six to eight of the lowest grades; this allows for excused absences. All of the homework is averaged in as one test grade.

Always get assignments, quizzes and tests graded and handed back the next class period. If students have to wait a week or two for their grades, the grades lose their importance.

SAMPLE SYLLABI

Provided by:

Chris *Bendixen Lake Michigan College*

Roger McCoach, *County College Morris*

Louise Olshan, *County College Morris*

MAT014 – BASIC ALGEBRA I   9/3/09
3 hrs./wk. – 0 cr.   BEGINNING FALL 2009

<u>Catalog description</u>:   A preparatory course in elementary algebra which includes rational numbers, polynomials, algebraic operations, first-degree equations, graphing, systems of linear equations, problem-solving and an introduction to quadratic equations.

<u>Prerequisite</u>: MAT009 or MAT011 or equivalent

<u>Text</u>: Bittinger, *Introductory Algebra,* 2009—County College of Morris Edition (Addison-Wesley).

<u>Supplementary materials</u>: Students may use their own calculators..

<u>Syllabus</u>

Period	Text sections	Topics
1		Placement test
2- 3	1.1-6	Algebraic expressions, operations on real numbers
4- 5	1.7-8	Properties of real numbers, simplifying algebraic expressions
6		Test no. 1
7- 8	2.1-3	Solving linear equations
9-11	2.4-7	Formulas, applications; solving linear inequalities
12		Test no. 2
13-14	4.1, 4.2a,b	Properties of exponents (concentration on positive exponents)
15	4.3-4	Polynomials, addition and subtraction of polynomials
16	4.5-6	Multiplication of polynomials
17	4.7, 4.8a	Polynomials with several variables, division by a monomial
18		Test no. 3
19-21	5.1-4	Introduction to factoring, factoring trinomials
22-23	5.5-6	Factoring binomials, general strategies
24	5.7	Solving quadratic equations by factoring
25		Test no. 4
26	3.1-3	Graphing linear equations, slope
27-28	7.1-4	Solving systems of linear equations, applications
29		Test no. 5
30		Review

MAT014 is intended to prepare students for courses such as MAT016 and MAT108, for which it is prerequisite.

Students are expected to adhere to the policies of the County College of Morris. These can be accessed at <u>www.ccm.edu/academics/policies.aspx</u>.

Lake Michigan College
Course Syllabus

I. COURSE DESCRIPTION

Discipline:	Mathematics
Title & Number:	Elementary Algebra, Math 095
Credit Hours:	4
Instructor:	Bendixen
Contact Hours:	4
Telephone:	
Office:	
Email Address:	
Blackboard URL:	
Prerequisites:	(1) Successful completion of Basic Math 090 (C or better) or score of 39 or higher on Asset Test/36 or higher on Compass Test or Passing Basic Math Proficiency Test.
	(2) Basic Skill Prerequisites: Reading and Math
Semester/Year:	Winter 2010

II. TEXTBOOK/MATERIALS

A. REQUIRED

1. Introductory Algebra, 10th Edition, by Bittinger. Addison-Wesley Publishers, 2007.
2. Pencils and Paper

B. OTHER MATERIALS

1. Computer assisted instruction available in computer labs (please ask instructor or assistant for help getting into the software)
2. Calculators may be used after Chapter 1 is completed.
3. Additional Web site for problems and help. www.interactmath.com

III. COURSE DESCRIPTION FROM CATALOG

The course covers all subjects normally taught in a one year beginning algebra course. Subjects covered: sets and numeration systems; the set of integers: multiplication and division, algebraic operations, equations; introduction to factoring; factoring techniques; basic fractional operations; addition, subtraction, multiplication and division of complex fractions; introduction to the rectangular coordinate system; systems of equations. Cannot be used to meet math graduation requirements for A.A., A.S., or A.A.S. degrees.

IV. GENERAL EDUCATION AREAS MET

This course supports the attainment of the general education requirements of Lake Michigan College. The above classroom goals are listed numerically below and meet the stated general education outcomes.

1. Communication: A – G
2. Critical Thinking: A – G
3. Mathematics: A – G

V. GOALS AND OBJECTIVES

Upon course completion, students should be able to:

A. Understand fundamental concepts of real numbers and algebraic expressions.

1. Evaluate algebraic expressions by substitution.
2. Translate phrases to algebraic expressions.
3. Graph rational numbers on a number line.
4. Convert a rational number to decimal notation.
5. Know meanings, symbols, and the use of $<$, $>$, $\leq$, and $\geq$.
6. Find the absolute value of a real number.
7. Add, subtract, multiply and divide real numbers.
8. Solve problems involving addition and subtraction of real numbers.
9. Find the opposite, or additive inverse of a real number.
10. Find the reciprocal of a real number.
11. Find equivalent fractions expressions, and simplify fractional expressions.
12. Identify the commutative, associative, identity, inverse, and distributive properties.
13. Collect like terms.
14. Simplify expressions by removing parentheses and collecting like terms.
15. Simplify expressions with parentheses inside parentheses.
16. Simplify expressions using rules for order of operations.

B. Solve equations.

1. Determine whether a given number is a solution to a given equation.
2. Solve equations using the addition principle and/or the multiplication principle.
3. Solve equations in which like terms may need to be collected.
4. Solve equations by first removing parentheses and collecting like terms.
5. Solve problems by translating into equations.
6. Solve problems involving percent.
7. Solve a formula for a specified letter.

C. Understand and use exponents and operations on polynomials.

1. Evaluate algebraic expressions containing exponents including those raised to the zero or first power.

2. Use the product and quotient rules for exponential expressions with like terms.

3. Change an expression with negative exponents to positive.

4. Use the power rule to raise powers to powers.

5. Raise a product to a power and a quotient to a power.

6. Evaluate a polynomial for a given value.

7. Identify terms, like terms, coefficients, and degree.

8. Collect the like terms of a polynomial.

9. Add, subtract, and multiply polynomials.

10. Multiply two polynomials by the FOIL method, and square binomials.

11. Divide a polynomial by a monomial, and by another polynomial.

D. Understanding and using factoring.

1. Find the common factor in a polynomial.

2. Factor by grouping for problems involving four terms.

3. Factor trinomials, trinomial squares, and difference of squares.

4. Find the principle square roots and their opposites of the whole numbers $(0^2–25^2)$

E. Understand and use the fundamental proportion of a rational expression.

1. Find all values for which a rational expression is undefined.

2. Simplify rational expressions to lowest terms.

3. Multiply and divide rational expressions and simplify.

4. Find least common denominators.

5. Add fractions, first finding the LCD.

6. Find the LCM of algebraic expressions by factoring.

7. Add and subtract rational expressions.

8. Simplify complex rational expressions.

F. Graphing linear equations.

1. Solve problems related to circle, bar, and line graphs.

2. Find and/or plot ordered pairs on a graph.

3. Determine whether a given ordered pair is a solution to a given equation.

4. Graph equations of the type $y = mx$ and $y = mx + b$

5. Find the intercept of a linear equation, and graph using intercepts.

6. Graph equations of the type $x = a$ or $y = b$.

7. Changing a number to a scientific notation number.

8. Changing a scientific notation number back to a decimal number.

9. Multiplying a scientific notation number by a scientific notation number.

10. Dividing a scientific notation number by a scientific notation number.

G. **Solving linear systems of two equations.**

1. Determine whether an ordered pair is a solution to a system of equations.

2. Solve systems of two linear equations in two variables by graphing.

3. Solve a system of two equations in two variables by the substitution method.

4. Solve a system of two equations in two variables using the elimination method.

VI. EXPECTED STUDENT OUTCOMES

During the semester you will be asked to participate in ungraded Assessment of Student Learning activities. Your instructor will use the information that you provide to better gauge your comprehension of course material; and, as appropriate, will modify how course material is presented in order to better prepare you to successfully complete graded assignments.

VII. INSTUCTIONAL METHODOLOGY

Methods of instruction used throughout the lecture course will include: lectures, written exercises, handouts, group work, question and answer sessions, and calculator exercises.

VIII. HOW TO WORK IN THIS COURSE

A. Attend class on a regular basis.

B. Read the corresponding section in the textbook that corresponds to the previous lecture.

C. Do the homework Exercises as assigned for each section.

Note: Answers to all odd-numbered section exercises as well as answers to every chapter review and test problem are given at the back of the book.

IX. DISRUPTIVE STUDENTS

Students who insist on carrying on conversations during class, or students who must listen to their music, will be asked to leave the class. Students who continue to not pay attention will be dropped from the class.

X. CHEATING AND/PLAGERISM

Any student caught copying off of another student's exam will receive an "E" for that exam score. The student's name will also be passed on to the Dean of Students, where, the Dean may take further actions (such as dismissal)

Xi. CALCULATORS

Calculators may be used after the chapter 1 exam. Cell phones may not be used as a calculator during exams. Cell phones have built-in cameras which could be used to send exam to friends or other students.

XII. GRADING CRITERIA AND REQUIREMENTS

A. TEST OUTLINE FOR COURSE

TEST NO.	TOPIC
1	Real Numbers and Algebraic Expressions
2	Solving Equations and Inequalities
3	Graphs of Equations and Inequalities; Scientific Notation
4	Polynomials: Operations
5/8	Polynomials: Factoring; Square Roots
6	Rational Expressions and Equations
7	Systems of Equations
FINAL EXAM	Chapters 1 through 8

Note: I may cover some of the chapters in different order than above.

B. FINAL EXAM

C. GRADING CRITERIA

1. 70% of final grade will be based on Chapter test scores.

2. 25% of final grade will be based on the Final Exam score.

3. Online homework using MYMATHLAB, 5%.

4. Students who withdraw from class through the 12th week of the semester will be assigned a grade of "W". Beyond the 12th week of the semester, students who withdraw will receive a grade of "E."

XIII. WRITING ACROSS THE CURRICULUM STRATEGY

Students will formulate and solve situational problems according to examples given in class, the textbook, computer, or video.

XIV. GRADING SCALE

PERCENTAGE	GRADE
90–100	A
80–89	B
70–79	C
60–69	D
Below 69	E

XV. MAKE-UP POLICY

Makeup exams will only be given to the student if prior arrangements have been made with the instructor, or, the student can provide a Doctors excuse for an illness. Students informing the instructor after the exam should have been taken will not be given a makeup exam. Students who miss an exam will get a score of zero on that exam.

XVI. ATTENDANCE POLICY/WITHDRAWAL POLICY

A. Attendance.

1. You are expected to attend class at your scheduled time.

2. Mindful of the diverse student body that Lake Michigan College serves, and the varied belief that its students represent, the College will make a reasonable effort to accommodate students who need to be excused from classes for the observance of religious holidays. This policy does not apply to students who knowingly register for classes scheduled to meet on days that consistently conflict with their day of worship, e.g., a student who signs up for Saturday classes when the student normally worships on Saturday.

3. College Withdrawal Policy

Students may withdraw from a course without instructor's permission through 80% of the course. Official withdrawal from a class will result in a grade of "W" on the student's transcript. A "W" grade will not be computed in the Lake Michigan College grade point average. The last date to withdraw with a guaranteed "W" is April 12.

B. **Cell phones, MUST** be shut off during class. These devises are very disruptive to the flow of the class. Any student who abuses this policy will be given a warning at first. If the cell phone goes off during sub sequential class meetings, the could start loosing exam points for each additional violation. With a maximum of 15% for an exam. Occasionally, a student may have an emergency situation where a cell phone is needed. Just let me know ahead of time. This will not count against the student. Absolutely NO texting during class.

XVII. DIVERSITY IN CLASSROOM

Lake Michigan College expects each instructor to address diversity within the classroom. Students will be exposed to a number of issues or concerns that may be considered as diversity issues. The instructor will address a variety of diversity issues throughout the duration of the course.

Lake Michigan College will strive to create an environment for its employees, students, and greater community which recognizes individual differences and commonalities, provides the exchange of diverse ideas, and encourages mutual understanding.

XVIII. ACADEMIC HONESTY POLICY

The principles of truth and honesty are recognized as fundamental to a community of teachers and scholars. Lake Michigan College expects that both faculty and students will honor these principles and in doing so protect the integrity of College grades. This means that all academic work will be done by the student to whom it is assigned without giving or receiving unauthorized aid of any kind. Instructors will exercise care in the planning and supervision of academic work so that honest effort will be positively encouraged. Cheating and plagiarism are the two most obvious violations of academic honesty. In brief, plagiarism is borrowing ideas, words, organization, etc. from another source or person and claiming them as original.

Any dishonest activity may result in failure of specific assignments or an entire course. Flagrant and/or repeated violations of Academic Honesty will result in disciplinary action up to and including expulsion from Lake Michigan College.

XIX. HOMEWORK POLICY/QUIZ POLICY

Students will work homework problems using MYMATHLAB software. A list of problems will be assigned. To be successful on a homework, the student has to score at least 70% on the section. Not all homework sections are graded, that is, some of the homework are reading assignments, some are PowerPoint presentations. Only the homework with problems will be scored and count towards the grade. Once the student has completed the homework, the student will submit the score. The score will go directly to me. Note, the problems for you may be different than those for someone else.

To get to the homework you do the following:

the internet address is: www.coursecompass.com

Enter the register as a student. You will need the course access number, it is **bendixen48992**

You will then need your access code. This will be the code that came with the text. If you did not get this code with your text, then you need to return the text and get a book packaged with the code.

Students who wish not to do the homework using the software will loose the 5% homework grade.

XX. Time Schedule

Each chapter will take approximately 5 or 6 class periods to cover. Expect an exam about every other week. Some chapters will be covered faster than others. As a general rule, expect about a section of a chapter per class period. Some of the chapters will be covered at a faster pace. (chapters 3 and 7). So expect an exam over these chapters about a week after they start.

The following pages are a list of suggested homework problems. For those students who are using MYMATHLAB, you can do these for additional studying.

ELEMENTARY ALGEBRA–COURSE 095 HOMEWORK ASSIGNMENT SCHEDULE

INTRODUCTORY ALGEBRA, 10th EDITION, By Bittinger

CHAPTER 1

1.1	pp. 58–63	pp. 64–65; # 9–53,
1.2	pp. 66–74	pp. 75–77; #10, #12, & 16–64
1.3	pp. 78–82	pp. 83–84; #3–63,
1.4	pp. 86–88	pp. 89–91; # 3–95, every 4th
1.5	pp. 93–96	pp. 97–98; #3–67, every 4th
1.6	pp. 100–105	pp. 106–107; #3–63, every 4th
1.7	pp. 109–117	pp. 118–121; # 9–23, odd # and #35 – 111, every 4th
1.8	pp. 122–127	pp. 128–130; # 3–79, every 4th

CHAPTER 1 TEST   Practice test: pp. 140–141; 1, 2, 4 – 28, 33 – 41

CHAPTER 2

2.1	pp. 138–141	pp. 142–143; #1–47, odd #
2.2	pp. 144–147	pp. 148–149; #1–35, odd #
2.3	pp. 150–157	pp. 158–161; #3–79, every 4th #
2.4	pp. 162–165	pp. 166–168; # 1–6; 9– 47 odd #
2.5	pp. 170–173	pp. 174–176; #1–11, odd # <u>and</u> 29, 31, 33, 39–47 odd
2.6	pp. 178–189	pp. 190–193; # 1–13, odd # <u>and</u> 19, 21

CHAPTER 2 TEST   Practice Test pp. 218–219;   #1 – 10, 25– 27; 31, 32, 37

CHAPTER 3

3.1	pp. 224–235	pp. 236 - 240; 1–53 odd #
3.2	pp. 243–248	pp. 249–254; # 3–53, odd #
3.3	pp. 255–261	pp. 262–265; #1–23 odd # and 39–57 odd #
4.2	pp. 315–320	pp. 323–324; 53–69, odd # and 75–83. odd #

CHAPTER 3 TEST   Practice Test p. 286–288; #15–25, 29, 30 and p. 386: 17–20

CHAPTER 4

4.1	pp. 304–309	pp. 310–312; # 3–111 every 4th
4.2	pp. 314–321	pp. 322; # 1–51, every 4th
4.3	pp. 337–334	pp. 335–339; #3–97, every 4th
4.4	pp. 341–344	pp. 345–347; #1–51, every 4th
4.5	pp. 349–352	pp. 353–354; #3–57. every 4th
4.6	pp. 356–361	pp. 363–365; #3–87, every 4th
4.7	pp. 367–370	pp. 371–374; #3–75, every 4th
4.8	pp. 376–379	pp. 380–381; #1–39, odd #

CHAPTER 4 TEST   Practice Test pp. 386–387; # 1–16 & 22–45

CHAPTER 5

5.1	pp. 392–398	pp. 399–400; # 7–23, odd #, <u>and</u> 35 – 51 odd
5.2	pp. 401–406	pp. 407 409; #3–61 every other odd
5.3	pp. 411–416	pp. 417–418; # 1–45 odd #
5.4	pp. 420–421	pp. 422–423; #1–45 odd
8.1	pp. 610–614	p. 615; # 1–19 odd
5.5	pp. 426–431	pp. 432–434; # 1–33 odd and 43–71 odd
5.6	pp. 436–439	pp. 440–442; #1–55 every other odd

CHAPTER 5/8 TEST   Practice Test pp. 469; # 2–21 and p. 660 #1–3

CHAPTER 6

6.1	pp. 472–478	pp. 479–481; #1–11, odd #, 25–63, odd
6.2	pp. 483–485	pp. 486–487; #1–35, odd #
6.3	pp. 488–489	pp. 490; #1 – 35, odd #
6.4	pp. 492–495	pp. 496–497; #1–47 odd #

| 6.5 | pp. 500–503 | pp. 504–505; #1–39 odd # |
| 6.8 | pp. 534–537 | p. 530; #1–17, odd # |

CHAPTER 6 TEST   Practice Test p. 554; #1–18

CHAPTER 7

7.1	pp. 560–564	pp.565–566; #1–25, odd #
7.2	pp. 567–570	pp. 571; #1–17 odd #
7.3	pp. 574–580	pp. 581–582; #1–33 odd

CHAPTER 7 TEST   Practice Test p. 607; 1–9

*** REQUIRED PRACTICE FINAL REVIEW*** (for preparation for actual final)
pp. 729–734; #2, 7, 8, 10, 12, 13, 16, 17, 32, 36, 37, 38, 39, 40, 45, 46, 48, 49, 50, 51, 52, 53, 55, 56, 58, 59, 60, 61, 78, 79

Calendar for Winter 2010 semester.

January 11	Classes Begin
January 18	Martin Luther King, Jr. Day - No Classes
January 19	Last Day to Add Classes
January 26	Last day to drop with a 100 % refund
February 18	Professional Development Day - No Classes
March 1–6	Spring Break - No Classes
April 2–4	College Closed - Recess - No Classes
May 1	LMC Classes End
May 5	Grades Available on Wavelink

TEACHING TIPS CORRELATED TO TEXTBOOK SECTIONS

Following is a listing of the objectives included in the Introductory Algebra *text, as well as specific teaching tips provided by the contributing professors.*

 R) **Prealgebra Review**

SECTION TITLES AND OBJECTIVES

R.1 Factoring and LCMs
Find all the factors of numbers and find prime factorizations of numbers ● Find the LCM of two or more numbers using prime factorizations

R.2 Fraction Notation
Find equivalent fraction expressions by multiplying by 1 ● Simplify fraction notation ● Add, subtract, multiply, and divide using fraction notation

R.3 Decimal Notation
Convert from decimal notation to fraction notation ● Add, subtract, multiply, and divide using decimal notation ● Round numbers to a specified decimal place

R.4 Percent Notation
Convert from percent notation to decimal notation ● Convert from percent notation to fraction notation ● Convert from decimal notation to percent notation ● Convert from fraction notation to percent notation

R.5 Exponential Notation and Order of Operations
Write exponential notation for a product ● Evaluate exponential expressions ● Simplify expressions using the rules for order of operations

R.6 Geometry
Find the perimeter of a polygon ● Find the area of a rectangle, a square, a parallelogram, and a triangle ● Find the length of a radius of a circle given the length of a diameter, and find the length of a diameter given the length of a radius; find the circumference and the area of a circle ● Find the volume of a rectangular solid

TEACHING TIPS

This chapter is useful for the overview of notation and its usage in different real-life examples.

Endre Borsos,
Miami-Dade Community College

◆ ◆ ◆

Be sure you have enough time to cover this chapter in your course outline. Even if you only have a class or two, much of this is worth the review time!

Gail G. Burkett,
Palm Beach Community College

◆ ◆ ◆

The key to any of the basic rules in algebra is in the application of the rules. Students do not always understand why these rules are important.

Bill Graesser,
Ivy Tech State College

◆◆◆

I sometimes introduce algebra as "arithmetic of unknown numbers." This helps me to explain to students how important it is for them to understand Chapter R.

- First, misconceptions in arithmetic are often at the heart of students' difficulties with the algebra. If we can identify and correct some of these misconceptions, we have removed some of the obstacles for success in the course.

- Second, because concepts in algebra often so closely parallel corresponding topics in arithmetic, a solid background in arithmetic is the best foundation a student can have for building an understanding of algebra.

Algebraic notations for multiplication need to be carefully introduced to students who have seen only the arithmetic notation 5×7. When they see that this notation will be confusing in a problem that also includes the variable X, they more readily accept the algebraic notations: $3 + 5 \cdot 7$ or $3 + 5(7)$.

Rosa Kavanaugh,
Ozarks Technical College

◆ ◆ ◆

Students have problems with applied problems. Here is where I use as many visual aids as possible. Sometimes it is pictures, sometimes it involves using other items like a cereal box.

Angela Walters,
Capitol College

Section R.1

I review the divisibility rules for 2, 3 and 5 before discussing prime numbers. Then I write the numbers 2–31 (and include 51) on the board. We then determine if these numbers are prime or composite.

Gail G. Burkett,
Palm Beach Community College

◆ ◆ ◆

Students generally have difficulty distinguishing between LCM and GCF and understanding why we learn them. I always use an example like 12 and 18. I have them list the factors of each and the first five multiples of each and then have them find the LCM and GCF and show how each is used (adding/ subtracting fractions—getting common denominators and simplifying fractions).

Jane Duncan Nesbit,
Columbia Union College

◆ ◆ ◆

It's helpful to have the table of primes in the classroom. If you have problems purchasing one, make an enlarged copy from the textbook and distribute it to the students.

Tatiana Sviridovsky,
Delaware County Community College

◆ ◆ ◆

Since my students are allowed to use calculators, I don't emphasize getting the lowest common denominator. I just ask them to get any common denominator, even if they have to resort to using the multiplication of both denominators as the common denominator. I tell them that the numbers can get very big, but they can use their calculator.

Sharon Testone,
Onondaga Community College

◆ ◆ ◆

I give problems/examples where the students have to verbally express what is meant by finding the prime factorization of a number, and give definitions for finding the LCD and GCF.

Angela Walters,
Capitol College

Section R.2

Students often forget to cancel factors of one before multiplying fractions. Students generally have trouble differentiating opposite and reciprocal.

Jane Duncan Nesbit,
Columbia Union College

◆ ◆ ◆

Students often have the impression that a mixed numeral is always a better form of an answer than an "improper" fraction. (In fact, this term is not used in these books). Some of them even believe that an improper fraction is not "simplified" unless it is expressed as a mixed numeral. It is helpful to inform algebra students that the mixed numeral is not necessarily the preferred form. I explain that because algebra uses both letters and numerals, there may be no way to determine which is larger: the numerator or the denominator of the fraction $\frac{5a}{2b}$. Thus in algebra, simplifying the fractional expression, rather than changing the form of improper fractions, is a critical issue.

Rosa Kavanaugh,
Ozarks Technical College

◆ ◆ ◆

It's easy to get delayed in this section. The students usually don't have a very strong background in these operations. Instead of spending too much time on it, I always insert practice sessions on fractions while we are covering chapters 1 and 2. While we do this practice, I always emphasize that understanding the steps is extremely important because we will use these same concepts when working with rational expressions later in the course.

Tatiana Sviridovsky,
Delaware County Community College

◆ ◆ ◆

When simplifying a fraction, instead of looking for the GCF I have them determine if the numerator and the denominator are both divisible by 2 or 5, and then we try 3, etc. I tell the students that this is NOT the most efficient way to simplify a fraction, but it does work if they have trouble finding the GCF. Again, since they are using calculators they can simplify a fraction this way.

Sharon Testone,
Onondaga Community College

◆ ◆ ◆

You can expect students to have problems understanding when they are allowed to cancel common factors in a fraction. Students have a difficult time understanding that they cannot cancel across sums.

Angela Walters,
Capitol College

Section R.3

Since the addition/subtraction of decimals is fairly easy and it is review, I don't spend any class time on this topic. I just assign such problems to do at home. Multiplication and especially division require more time. It's very important to include the problems where one of the digits in the quotient is zero which this section doesn't include (i.e. $9.197 \div 3.4$; the answer is 2.705).

Tatiana Sviridovsky,
Delaware County Community College

Section R.4

As a visual aid, I write on the board, "When asked for a peRcent, move the decimal point right. When asked for a decimaL, move it left."

Gail G. Burkett,
Palm Beach Community College

◆ ◆ ◆

Students often forget which direction to move the decimal point when converting from decimal to percent or percent to decimal. I tell them when going to a percent, they move two places to the right. The word percent has an R in the center, reminding us to move to the right. When changing to a decimal, they move to the left, and the word decimal has an "L" at the end reminding us to move to the left.

Sharon Testone,
Onondaga Community College

Section R.5

I begin this objective with $12 \div 3 \cdot 4$ and discuss the mnemonic devices, warning the students about the MD and AS.

Gail G. Burkett,
Palm Beach Community College

◆ ◆ ◆

Order of operations is understandably a difficult topic for many students. I explain to them that we learn to read from left to right and thus have trained our minds to process information in that order. Algebraic order requires that we retrain our minds to think in a different order. Students need to hear that even if they fully understand the rules, extensive practice is necessary or our minds tend to revert to the more familiar left to right order.

Usually some students have already seen the acronym for order of operations:

P
E
MD
AS

But students still often mistakenly believe that multiplication has a higher priority than division and addition higher than subtraction. It is important to emphasize that multiplication and division are on the same level and thus have the same priority. One is not always automatically done before the other. The order of these pairs is from left to right, as we have been trained to read and tend to think.

Rosa Kavanaugh,
Ozarks Technical College

◆ ◆ ◆

This material will be covered in sections 1.8 and 4.1; I don't do it until that time.

Tatiana Sviridovsky,
Delaware County Community College

◆ ◆ ◆

Order of operation is an area where students tend to have problems. They want to simplify in the order the problem is written, from left to right, and not with respect to the order of operations.

Angela Walters,
Capitol College

Section R.6

Students seem to have a hard time remembering formulas. I urge them to copy them on index cards as a study tool.

Gail G. Burkett,
Palm Beach Community College

◆ ◆ ◆

Don't make the geometry a matter of memorizing formulas. Make sure students get the concept of perimeter, area, and volume. Have students find the perimeter, area and volume of the classroom or some smaller object in the classroom.

Jane Duncan Nesbit,
Columbia Union College

◆ ◆ ◆

Students often have difficulty memorizing formulas. Whenever there are formulas that students need to memorize, I give them a strategy for memorizing the formulas as they do their homework. I tell them that each time they use the formula, it is important that they write the formula <u>first</u> and then substitute the given info. Many students instead tend to merely write the result after substitution and miss the learning benefits of the writing process. I explain that the repeated writing of the original formula as they use it actually helps them to remember it.

Rosa Kavanaugh,
Ozarks Technical College

◆ ◆ ◆

In problems where the student is asked to find volume or area, I use a common item like a cereal box to help the student see what is meant by the terms volume and area.

Angela Walters,
Capitol College

Introduction to Real Numbers and Algebraic Expressions

SECTION TITLES AND OBJECTIVES

1.1 Introduction to Algebra
Evaluate algebraic expressions by substitution ● Translate phrases to algebraic expressions

1.2 The Real Numbers
State the integer that corresponds to a real-world situation ● Graph rational numbers on a number line ● Convert from fraction notation for a rational number to decimal notation ● Determine which of two real numbers is greater and indicate which, using < or >; given an inequality like $a > b$, write another inequality with the same meaning. Determine whether an inequality like $-3 \leq 5$ is true or false ● Find the absolute value of a real number

1.3 Addition of Real Numbers
Add real numbers without using a number line ● Find the opposite, or additive inverse, of a real number ● Solve applied problems involving addition of real numbers

1.4 Subtraction of Real Numbers
Subtract real numbers and simplify combinations of additions and subtractions ● Solve applied problems involving subtraction of real numbers

1.5 Multiplication of Real Numbers
Multiply real numbers ● Solve applied problems involving multiplication of real numbers

1.6 Division of Real Numbers
Divide integers ● Find the reciprocal of a real number ● Divide real numbers ● Solve applied problems involving division of real numbers

1.7 Properties of Real Numbers
Find equivalent fraction expressions and simplify fraction expressions ● Use the commutative and associative laws to find equivalent expressions ● Use the distributive laws to multiply expressions like 8 and $x - y$ ● Use the distributive laws to factor expressions like $4x - 12 + 24y$ ● Collect like terms

1.8 Simplifying Expressions; Order of Operations
Find an equivalent expression for an opposite without parentheses, where an expression has several terms ● Simplify expressions by removing parentheses and collecting like terms ● Simplify expressions with parentheses inside parentheses ● Simplify expressions using rules for order of operations

TEACHING TIPS

The introduction to algebra in a beginning or introductory algebra class should be as smooth as possible. Don't start by throwing definitions to the students since they tend to get disoriented by the language of algebra. Be sure to let students know where algebra is used in real life and in what valuable circumstances it can be helpful.

Endre Borsos,
Miami-Dade Community College

◆ ◆ ◆

Show the patterns in subtraction and multiplication to explain why the sign rules apply.

Jane Duncan Nesbit,
Columbia Union College

◆ ◆ ◆

Some students seem to believe that it is always legitimate to assume that $x = 1$. They seem to misinterpret the explanation that x means $1x^1$ to mean $x = 1$. An explanation that emphasizes terminology with distinction between the coefficient, the exponent and the value of x should help to resolve this misunderstanding.

Rosa Kavanaugh,
Ozarks Technical College

◆ ◆ ◆

I have the students complete over 60 problems of adding integers before I move on to work with decimals and fractions. I do the same for subtracting integers. I teach multiplication and division at the same time, because the rule is the same. This saves time. (I try not to teach adding and subtracting integers the same day. They need to know the rules for adding before they can subtract, so I like to give them time to practice.)

Sharon Testone,
Onondaga Community College

◆ ◆ ◆

I find it useful to talk about the history of numbers when going through the various number systems. For example, I mention that the Romans did not have a number to represent 0. Then I ask the students why we need to have negative numbers and zero. (Use a checking account as an example.)

Angela Walters,
Capitol College

Section 1.1

I highlight and do several examples of the subtraction translations that are NOT straightforward e.g. less than, take from, and subtract from.

Gail G. Burkett,
Palm Beach Community College

◆ ◆ ◆

Stress the importance of translating words into algebraic expressions and evaluating expressions/formulas.

Jane Duncan Nesbit,
Columbia Union College

Sometimes students need two lessons on translating phrases to algebraic expressions. I usually create worksheets so that students can get extra practice during their laboratories.

Deloria Nanze-Davis,
University of Texas, Brownsville, Texas Southmost College

◆ ◆ ◆

The text contains a good list of key words on page 59. Example 9 addresses the confusion caused by the phrase, "less than." I use the analogy for students that in translating from one language to another, say English to Spanish, it is not enough to merely translate word for word in the original order. Usually there are one or more students who have learned a foreign language and can verify my statement. I explain that in translation of language there are also rules of order to learn. In mathematics, the phrase "less than" changes the order so "5 less than x" becomes "$x - 5$."

Rosa Kavanaugh,
Ozarks Technical College

◆ ◆ ◆

I always tell the students to give me some key words associated with the word "Algebra" (they usually say "letter", "equation", "variable").

To get started with the definitions of variable and constant, I have them do the following exercise: "If I teach two or three sections of the same course, and every student gets a copy of the syllabus from me, is the number of chapters in the syllabus a constant or a variable? How about the number of copies of the syllabus that I have to prepare for each class?"

I always ask them to compare two problems like #19 and #31 on page 61.

Surprisingly many students don't understand the meaning of the word "Evaluate"; therefore, be sure to emphasize this term.

Tatiana Sviridovsky,
Delaware County Community College

Section 1.2

Make sure students understand ordering inequalities. We usually read from left to right so '<' is less than but it can be read from the other side which is equivalent.

When presenting absolute value, make sure students understand the definition! Don't let them just memorize that the number becomes positive. This understanding will become useful when learning absolute value equations and inequalities.

Jane Duncan Nesbit,
Columbia Union College

◆ ◆ ◆

Students have difficulty remembering which symbol $>$ or $<$ is the less than or greater than symbol. I tell them that the $<$ looks like an "L" and stands for less than. Another way to remember the difference is that the open end always opens toward the larger number.

Students have problems realizing that -5 is less than -1. I use the number line to show them that when comparing two integers, the one to the right is always larger.

Sharon Testone,
Onondaga Community College

◆ ◆ ◆

It helps students to see the hierarchy of the number systems if you draw a chart showing their relationship. There is a nice chart on page 68 in the text.

Angela Walters,
Capitol College

Section 1.3

Many students struggle with addition of signed numbers. The traditional rules on page 76 are certainly a mathematically correct explanation, as is the number line model. I have found that a number of my adult students relate to and are successful with the checkbook analogy of addition of signed numbers. In this model, $75 + (-37)$ represents: "You have $75 in your checking account and write a check for $37. What is the balance in your account?" Students are comfortable with the $38 balance. Likewise, $58 + (-62)$ is interpreted as: "You have $58 in your checking account and write a check for $62. What is the balance in your account?" Most students answer that the account would be $4 overdrawn. (One student did answer that the account would be $29 overdrawn due to the $25 service charge.)

Students often continue to struggle with -3^2 vs. $-(3)^2$. Several approaches have proven meaningful to a number of these students. On page 77, Dr. Bittinger defines $-a$ as the "opposite of a." This terminology tends to be less intimidating to students than "additive inverse." Then the opposite of a non-zero number has the opposite sign. If students are permitted to use a scientific calculator at this point, the "$(-)$" key or the "$+/-$" key could be called the "opposite key."

Rosa Kavanaugh,
Ozarks Technical College

Section 1.4

The most difficult type of subtraction problem is in the form: $-14 - 6$. I approach this problem two ways.

a. I speak clearly about negative signs and subtraction signs. I indicate that we need to see an "operation." In this case, the operation is subtraction. I usually circle the subtraction sign and then ask whether the 6 is a positive or negative number. Once we all agree that the 6 is a positive number and the operation is subtraction, we then follow the rules. We "add the opposite" so the problem becomes: $-14 + (-6) = -20$.

b. If students still cannot understand the problem, I use an example about their checking accounts. "Suppose your checking account is $14 in the hole or $-\$14$ and you write another check for $6. You have to subtract that $6 from the $-\$14$. I then ask for the balance in their checking accounts. Most of the students can understand this analogy. Once dollar signs are included, they become better at the mathematics. (We often joke about the bank fees and the potential for arrest if we keep up this practice of writing bad checks.)

Sharon Testone,
Onondaga Community College

Section 1.5

I prefer to teach sections 1.5 and 1.6 before sections 1.3 and 1.4. I do this so the students only have to memorize three lines:

1. Change any double signs to a single sign using the multiplication rules.
2. When the signs are the same add and keep the sign.
3. When the signs are different, subtract and take the sign of the bigger number.

Gail G. Burkett,
Palm Beach Community College

◆ ◆ ◆

We may define "factor" as "write as multiplication." Some students may claim that $5x + 15$ may factored as $5 \cdot x + 5 \cdot 3$ and that is written as multiplication. One good explanation would certainly be a reference to algebraic order. Since the addition would be done last, this form is in fact an addition rather than a multiplication. This explanation might be too abstract, however, for the algebra novice. Perhaps a more meaningful explanation for such a student would be a reference to the problem of factoring 30. Although it is true that $30 = 10 + 20 = 2 \cdot 5 + 4 \cdot 5$, students seem to understand that this last form is not "factored."

Rosa Kavanaugh,
Ozarks Technical College

◆ ◆ ◆

Take time when explaining these problems similar to the ones on page 97 (#67–74). Just by looking, the students find them extremely simple (especially if they are allowed to use a calculator).

Tatiana Sviridovsky,
Delaware County Community College

Section 1.6

Keep reminding the students that there is a difference between $\frac{5}{0}$ and $\frac{0}{5}$; otherwise, even in Calculus courses the students will still be giving the wrong answers.

Tatiana Sviridovsky,
Delaware County Community College

◆ ◆ ◆

Students sometimes have problems with division of fractions. They will usually remember to change the division sign to multiplication but they forget to invert the denominator, especially if the denominator is not a fraction.

Angela Walters,
Capitol College

Section 1.8

If students are shown that using the "opposite key" is analogous to multiplying by negative one, then simplifying expressions like -3^2 and $-(3)^2$ can be presented as an algebraic order question. That is, -3^2 represents an exponent and a multiplication by negative one so the exponentiation is performed first. The expression $-(3)^2$ corresponds to a multiplication by negative one inside parentheses and an exponent, so the multiplication is performed first. This discussion could accompany the "Calculator Corner" on page 126.

Rosa Kavanaugh,
Ozarks Technical College

◆ ◆ ◆

For order of operations, I always use Please Excuse My Dear Aunt Sally. PEMDAS refers to parentheses or any grouping symbol, exponents, multiplication, division, addition and subtraction. A pitfall here is that students think that multiplication takes priority over division and that addition takes priority over subtraction. Instructors need to emphasize that multiplication and division are to be completed from left to right as are addition and subtraction.

Example: $6 \div (3)(2)$

Many students simplify $6 \div (3)(2)$ as 1 because they completed the multiplication first. They may have made an error because they think multiplication takes priority over division or because they think the ( ) around the numbers to indicate multiplication are the "grouping symbols" that needed to be done first.

Sharon Testone,
Onondaga Community College

◆ ◆ ◆

When simplifying expressions, stress that when there is a $(-)$ sign in front of a parenthesis, all quantities inside are multiplied by -1.

Angela Walters,
Capitol College

2 Solving Equations and Inequalities

SECTION TITLES AND OBJECTIVES

2.1   Solving Equations: The Addition Principle
Determine whether a given number is a solution of a given equation ● Solve equations using the addition principle

2.2   Solving Equations: The Multiplication Principle
Solve equations using the multiplication principle

2.3   Using the Principles Together
Solve equations using both the addition and the multiplication principles ● Solve equations in which like terms may need to be collected ● Solve equations by first removing parentheses and collecting like terms; solve equations with infinite number of solutions and equations with no solutions.

2.4   Formulas
Evaluate a formula ● Solve a formula for a specified letter

2.5   Applications of Percent
Solve applied problems involving percent

2.6   Applications and Problem Solving
Solve applied problems by translating to equations

2.7   Solving Inequalities
Determine whether a given number is a solution of an inequality ● Graph an inequality on a number line ● Solve inequalities using the addition principle ● Solve inequalities using the multiplication principle ● Solve inequalities using the addition and multiplication principles together

2.8   Applications and Problem Solving with Inequalities
Translate number sentences to inequalities ● Solve applied problems using inequalities

TEACHING TIPS

Always start with the Pretest, and work through the examples as an introduction to this chapter. Equations and their properties are one of the few topics that students will need to master in depth.

Endre Borsos,
Miami-Dade Community College

◆ ◆ ◆

You will need extra time for problem solving (word problems)! I stress the importance of declaring the variable so you know what you are looking for and then translating the words into an equation. I spend a whole class period just setting up the equations for word problems with students' help and leading. Many students may want to take short cuts and solve without declaring the variable and/or setting up an equation, but stress the importance of learning the process and developing the skills to set up the problem. Show this importance in your grading by giving two points for the set up and two points for solving.

Jane Duncan Nesbit,
Columbia Union College

◆ ◆ ◆

If a student is to master this chapter, the word "solve" must have meaning. This is a good opportunity to connect the mathematical word to the common English word. We hear about "solving a mystery" in a variety of situations (e.g. "Who robbed the bank?"). The meaning is that there is something that we don't know. In algebra, when we are asked to "Solve $3x + 5 = 5(x - 1)$" we should realize that there is a "mystery" (i.e. "What is x?"). Students who grasp this can understand that there is a goal and can recognize when they have reached it.

Rosa Kavanaugh,
Ozarks Technical College

◆ ◆ ◆

I skip any of the word problems that could be done more easily with two variables instead of one and come back to those problems after we learn elimination and substitution.

Sharon Testone,
Onondaga Community College

◆ ◆ ◆

When solving equations, many students try using trial and error to find the solution. They resist using the steps for solving an equation.

It is important to stress the idea of checking the obtained solution. Often, students will neglect this step because they do not see the significance of it.

Angela Walters,
Capitol College

Section 2.1

Fractions intimidate so many students. It is difficult but important to convince them that an **equation with fractions** is the best kind of problem with fractions that they could encounter. They need to see that the first step in solving an equation with fractions is to clear the fractions. If they can master this in Chapter 2, then they will find the rational equations in Chapter 6 much less difficult.

Rosa Kavanaugh,
Ozarks Technical College

Section 2.3

Make sure you assign AT LEAST the odd problems for homework. This section is so important in the long run.

Gail G. Burkett,
Palm Beach Community College

◆ ◆ ◆

An equation is a balance, like a teeter-totter with the equal sign as the fulcrum. Both the addition principle and the multiplication principle require that, to maintain that balance, whatever is done to one side of the equation must also be done to the other side.

Rosa Kavanaugh,
Ozarks Technical College

◆ ◆ ◆

To wrap up the material on equations, we have the "Be a Teacher" activity. I prepare and distribute a quiz "taken" by a bad student and my students must correct it for bonus points. The mistakes are usually the common ones: For the first example: $13 - x = 6$, I give the answer as $-x = 6$. For the second equation: $7(x - 4) = 38$, I show the work as $7x - 4 = 38$. For the third equation: $3x - (x + 2) = -10$, I show the work as $3x - x + 2 = 10$. Final: $6x = 3$, I give the answer as 2. The students like this activity and participate well.

Tatiana Sviridovsky,
Delaware County Community College

◆ ◆ ◆

Silly as it may sound, it is important for students to understand that an '=' indicates that what is on the left side of the equation is the same as what is on the right hand side of the equation.

Angela Walters,
Capitol College

Section 2.4

The translating for success page is a great tool for practice in this section.

Gail G. Burkett,
Palm Beach Community College

◆ ◆ ◆

Stress the importance of inverses and other properties learned in Chapter 1 that will help them ease into Section 2.4 (solving formulas for the indicated variable).

Jane Duncan Nesbit,
Columbia Union College

◆ ◆ ◆

I usually assign a small project in this section ("Understanding Your Electric Bill", "Why I Paid That Much for Gas", "Will the Round Mirror Fit There?") to help the students see the use of the formulas in real life.

Tatiana Sviridovsky,
Delaware County Community College

◆ ◆ ◆

Formulas are extremely difficult for students. I try to show them all of the formulas that just have multiplication, that just have division, that just have addition, and that just have subtraction before introducing more complicated examples. I talk about which variable we are trying to find. Additionally, I write a similar problem next to it with one variable and constants and solve both at the same time (emphasizing the steps)

Example: $ax + by = c$

Solve for x. $2x + 3 = 6$

Sharon Testone,
Onondaga Community College

Section 2.5

I also show the $\frac{\%}{100} = \frac{is}{of}$ method of solving the simple percent translation problems.

Gail G. Burkett,
Palm Beach Community College

◆ ◆ ◆

Many students will try to use the proportion method in Section 2.5 (percent applications) but try to help them see the other way too.

Jane Duncan Nesbit,
Columbia Union College

◆ ◆ ◆

Students have difficulty labeling the unknowns in an application where there is more than one unknown but it is desirable to write an equation with only one unknown. The rule of thumb that has seemed to help many students is: "Choose primary unknown to be the one about which you have the least information." Thus for Example 6 in Section 2.6, the primary unknown is the back angle since there is information given about the other two angles.

Rosa Kavanaugh,
Ozarks Technical College

Section 2.6

Although students usually groan at this section, it is vital for these applications to be integrated!

Gail G. Burkett,
Palm Beach Community College

◆ ◆ ◆

Go over the tips for problem solving (such as those on pages 181 and 191). Keep referring the students back to these steps when doing problems in class.

Angela Walters,
Capitol College

Section 2.7

A common mistake students make is to graph $3 > x$ as $x > 3$. Make sure they read the inequality from the variable side.

Jane Duncan Nesbit,
Columbia Union College

◆ ◆ ◆

I remind the students to switch the direction of the inequality symbol when both sides of the inequality are multiplied or divided by a negative number. I also emphasize that a dangerous habit is to switch the direction of the inequality just because there is a negative number in the problem. Thus, show them the difference between the solution of $-9x < 18$ and $9x < -18$.

Tatiana Sviridovsky,
Delaware County Community College

◆ ◆ ◆

Students have problems with inequalities because they don't know which direction to draw the arrow to show the solution set. If they solve the inequality with the variable on the left-hand side, the inequality will be pointing in the same direction that their arrow is supposed to point. Of course, they should always pick a point in the solution set and complete the check. It has to be emphasized that if the solution is $x > 2$, they should NOT check with 2. They need to choose 3, 4, 100, etc.

Students always forget to change the direction of the inequality when multiplying or dividing across the inequality with a negative number. Sometimes they switch the direction of the inequality when they multiply or divide by a positive number and get a negative answer. They have to know that the "act" of multiplying or dividing by the negative number causes the change. The sign of the answer could be anything.

Sharon Testone,
Onondaga Community College

Graphs of Linear Equations

SECTION TITLES AND OBJECTIVES

3.1 Graphs and Applications of Linear Equations
Plot points associated with ordered pairs of numbers; determine the quadrant in which a point lies • Find the coordinates of a point on a graph • Determine whether an ordered pair is a solution of an equation with two variables • Graph linear equations of the type $y = mx + b$ and $Ax + By = C$, identifying the y-intercept • Solve applied problems involving graphs of linear equations

3.2 More with Graphing and Intercepts
Find the intercepts of a linear equation, and graph using intercepts • Graph equations equivalent to those of the type $x = a$ and $y = b$

3.3 Slope and Applications
Given the coordinates of two points on a line, find the slope of the line, if it exists • Find the slope of a line from an equation • Find the slope, or rate of change, in an applied problem involving slope

3.4 Equations of Lines
Given an equation in the form $y = mx + b$, find the slope and the y-intercept; find an equation of a line when the slope and the y-intercept are given • Find an equation of a line when the slope and a point on the line are given • Find an equation of a line when two points on the line are given

3.5 Graphing Using the Slope and the y-intercept
Use the slope and the y-intercept to graph a line

3.6 Parallel and Perpendicular Lines
Determine whether the graphs of two linear equations are parallel • Determine whether the graphs of two linear equations are perpendicular

3.7 Graphing Inequalities in Two Variables
Determine whether an ordered pair of numbers is a solution of an inequality in two variables • Graph linear inequalities

TEACHING TIPS

Graphing can be a hard topic for students to master. Show students the real life use of graphs and their interpretations.

Endre Borsos,
Miami-Dade Community College

◆ ◆ ◆

My students have always found it very confusing to be given two options for graphing using slope-intercept (i.e. either up and right or down and left for positive slope). They seem to be more confident if they don't have to make that choice. I recommend that they avoid the potential confusion by moving up or down from the y-intercept depending on whether the sign of the slope is positive or negative. Then they can **always move over to the right.** I explain to them that the fraction does, in fact, give them instructions for doing this. For example, I ask them to read the fraction $-\frac{3}{5}$. They say "negative three-fifths" or "negative three over five." The second wording then tells them how to move from the y-intercept if they replace the word "negative" by "down" when they read it: **"down three, over five."** By the same convention, a slope of $\frac{1}{4}$ instructs them to move **"up one, over four."** Students seem to find this explanation very helpful.

One of the most common errors in plotting points is interchanging the x- and y-coordinates. If time and the classroom permit, it is helpful to ask students to plot one or two points on their papers before leaving class. This allows the instructor to identify and redirect students who have a tendency to make this mistake.

Rosa Kavanaugh,
Ozarks Technical College

◆ ◆ ◆

Instructors should draw all graphs on the overhead using grids. Students often put points in the "boxes" instead of the intersections. They have no idea how to graph when the instructor just sketches something on the board. I place my grid paper under the overhead roll and just roll up a clean portion when I am finished with my current graph. All I need is one piece of grid overhead, which I made by using tables in WORD.

Another alternative is to use WINPLOT, which can be downloaded for free. It will allow you to make grids, plot points, and draw graphs. All of this can be accomplished in that program or the graph can be copied to a clipboard and pasted into a Word or PowerPoint document. It is a great way to include graphs in quizzes, exams, etc.

For graphing, I emphasize 3 types: (I ensure that students label each axis, label their lines, and put arrows on the lines to show that they continue beyond the graph.)

Type 1: $y = mx + b$ form.

$y = 2x + 3$

(I graph using a table of values.)

I think students have the most difficulty understanding that they can choose their own numbers when graphing and that different students can have different tables of values.

Type 2: $ax + by = c$ form.

$2x + 3y = 6$

I find two points by using intercepts. I find the third point by substituting the opposite of the x-intercept into the equation and solving for y.

For this example: $x = 3$, $y = 0$, and $x = 0$, $y = 2$.

To find the third point, I would use $x = -3$.

$2(-3) + 3y = 6, 3y = 12$, so $y = 4$. Now we have an integer to plot.

By choosing the opposite of the x value, you will always come up with an integer to graph instead of a fraction. (NOTE: students often do have problems plotting intercepts.)

Type 3: $x = 3$ or $y = 2$

I tell students to put a point on the axis given at the "number" mentioned. So to graph $x = 3$, we would put a point on the x–axis at 3 and then put a point above and below that point where x is still 3. We then draw our line through the "axis" given at that point mentioned. (This seems to help!)

Sharon Testone,
Onondaga Community College

◆ ◆ ◆

In my experience, students are familiar with plotting points in the Cartesian plane. So, there may not be a need to spend much time on this topic beyond refreshing their understanding with a couple of examples.

Angela Walters,
Capitol College

◆ ◆ ◆

Use a graphing calculator to develop the fact that parallel lines have the same slope and perpendicular lines have opposite reciprocal slopes. Graph many lines, showing the equations in slope-intercept form, and allow the students to discover these facts.

Roy West,
Robeson Community College

Section 3.1

There is a lot of material in this section. Plan EXTRA TIME to cover 3.1

I give a summary/guideline for picking an easy x (or y) for the T charts.

Scenario 1: Given slope intercept form with no fractions, pick: x values of 1, 0 and -1.

Scenario 2: Given slope intercept form with a fractional coefficient of x, pick: the denominator, 0 and negative denominator

Scenario 3: Given standard form, pick intercept 0's

Scenario 4: Given only one variable, don't pick anything; it's either vertical or horizontal.

Gail G. Burkett,
Palm Beach Community College

❖ ❖ ❖

Most students can read and interpret graphs correctly. Spend time on the rectangular coordinate system and ordered pairs.

Jane Duncan Nesbit,
Columbia Union College

❖ ❖ ❖

Give the students an example of using two coordinates for locating the correct seat at the concert: the row number and the seat number.

Stress that the numbering of the quadrants is standard and doesn't vary from book to book; therefore, they have to memorize it.

Tatiana Sviridovsky,
Delaware County Community College

Section 3.2

Be careful of this common mistake—graphing a vertical line for $y = 3$ since the y-axis is vertical. I stress rewriting the equation as $y + 0x = 3$ and substituting values of x.

Stress the concept of "infinitely many solutions exist for a two variable linear equation but all of the points fall on a unique straight line."

Be aware of this common mistake—when finding x and y-intercepts, students substitute a zero for the wrong variable or they plot the point using both the x and y they get from substituting zero first for x and then for y.

Jane Duncan Nesbit,
Columbia Union College

❖ ❖ ❖

Students often confuse the equations of vertical and horizontal lines. Remind them that the equations "appear" opposite:

Vertical lines—parallel to the y-axis—have the equation $x = a$.

Horizontal lines—parallel to the x-axis—have the equation $y = b$.

Annette Wiesner,
University of Wisconsin-Parkside

Section 3.3

A quick and fun tool for remembering vertical and horizontal slopes: You can make a Z, for zero, out of the horizontal line. You can make an N, for no slope or undefined, out of the vertical line.

Gail G. Burkett,
Palm Beach Community College

❖ ❖ ❖

Spend a lot of time with the concept of slope and the real life applications of these two variable linear equations.

Jane Duncan Nesbit,
Columbia Union College

◆ ◆ ◆

Be sure that your students understand clearly which lines are horizontal and which ones are vertical, because some of them don't know the difference.

Tatiana Sviridovsky,
Delaware County Community College

◆ ◆ ◆

It is important that the idea of slope as a rate of change is understood by students. There are some good examples on pages 260 and 261 in the textbook. I stress that there are many real world applications for using slope as a rate of change, and I give them some more examples beyond what is given in the text.

Angela Walters,
Capitol College

◆ ◆ ◆

When beginning slope, relate positive and negative slope to "uphill" and "downhill". This makes an easy transition for students to understand zero slope (horizontal line).

Annette Wiesner,
University of Wisconsin-Parkside

Section 3.5

When graphing by using the slope and the y-intercept, show examples when the slope is an integer and assign similar problems for the homework (page 279, problems #21–24). Not all students will realize without assistance that when we consider the slope as rise over run, then the integer slope should be put over 1. Also, don't forget to include an example with a negative slope.

Tatiana Sviridovsky,
Delaware County Community College

4 Polynomials: Operations

SECTION TITLES AND OBJECTIVES

4.1 Integers as Exponents

Tell the meaning of exponential notation ● Evaluate exponential expressions with exponents of 0 and 1 ● Evaluate algebraic expressions containing exponents ● Use the product rule to multiply exponential expressions with like bases ● Use the quotient rule to divide exponential expressions with like bases ● Express an exponential expression involving negative exponents with positive exponents

4.2 Exponents and Scientific Notation

Use the power rule to raise powers to powers ● Raise a product to a power and a quotient to a power ● Convert between scientific notation and decimal notation ● Multiply and divide using scientific notation ● Solve applied problems using scientific notation

4.3 Introduction to Polynomials

Evaluate a polynomial for a given value of the variable ● Identify the terms of a polynomial ● Identify the like terms of a polynomial ● Identify the coefficients of a polynomial ● Collect the like terms of a polynomial ● Arrange a polynomial in descending order, or collect the like terms and then arrange in descending order ● Identify the degree of each term of a polynomial and the degree of the polynomial ● Identify the missing terms of a polynomial ● Classify a polynomial as a monomial, binomial, trinomial, or none of these

4.4 Addition and Subtraction of Polynomials

Add polynomials ● Simplify the opposite of a polynomial ● Subtract polynomials ● Use polynomials to represent perimeter and area

4.5 Multiplication of Polynomials

Multiply monomials ● Multiply a monomial and any polynomial ● Multiply two binomials ● Multiply any two polynomials

4.6 Special Products

Multiply two binomials mentally using the FOIL method ● Multiply the sum and the difference of two terms mentally ● Square a binomial mentally ● Find special products when polynomial products are mixed together

4.7 Operations with Polynomials in Several Variables

Evaluate a polynomial in several variables for given values of the variables ● Identify the coefficients and the degrees of the terms of a polynomial and the degree of a polynomial ● Collect like terms of a polynomial ● Add polynomials ● Subtract polynomials ● Multiply polynomials

4.8 Division of Polynomials

Divide a polynomial by a monomial ● Divide a polynomial by a divisor that is a binomial

TEACHING TIPS

I usually give the students a handout of the special products so that they don't have to continually refer to the book.

Deloria Nanze-Davis,
University of Texas, Brownsville, Texas Southmost College

◆ ◆ ◆

Subtracting polynomials—many students forget to add the opposite of every term. Dividing polynomials—spend lots of time showing how it is similar to real number division. Evaluating polynomials—I use the skeleton method and put a pair of parentheses wherever there is a variable and then I substitute the appropriate number in for the appropriate variable and use the order of operations to simplify.

Jane Duncan Nesbit,
Columbia Union College

Section 4.1

This section is VITAL to introductory algebra and contains A LOT of material.

Make sure you allow for extra time on section 4.1 and assign at least the odd problems for homework, including #111.

Gail G. Burkett,
Palm Beach Community College

◆ ◆ ◆

Beware of this common mistake—not keeping the base, but actually dividing or multiplying it.

Spend time developing the idea and concept of a negative exponent and a zero exponent. Use patterns to justify.

Jane Duncan Nesbit,
Columbia Union College

◆ ◆ ◆

I usually cover 4.1 and 4.2 during the same lecture (our syllabus doesn't include the scientific notation). I prepare and distribute a handout containing <u>all</u> definitions related to the exponents and their properties, as well as the following reminders:

a) simplified algebraic expressions cannot have negative exponents in them

b) the exponent not written is 1, not zero (I usually ask them to simplify $s \cdot s^3$ because the common wrong answer is s^3)

c) the shortcut for simplifying $\left(\frac{a}{b}\right)^{-n}$ *is to change it to* $\left(\frac{b}{a}\right)^n$. We use this summary as we move through 4.1 and 4.2

Tatiana Sviridovsky,
Delaware County Community College

◆ ◆ ◆

I like to teach students about division of exponents before I talk about exponents of zero and one because I use division to "show" why anything to the zero power is 1 or anything to the first power is itself.

Example: $\dfrac{2^3}{2^3} = 2^0$ using the rule for division or $\dfrac{8}{8} = 1$.

Example: $\dfrac{2^4}{2^3} = 2^1$ using the rule for division or $\dfrac{16}{8} = 2$.

Students know that $2x + 3x = 5x$, but as soon as we start talking about multiplying variables, and thus adding exponents as in $(2x)(3x) = 6x^2$, they tell me that $2x + 3x = 5x^2$. Additionally, they will tell me that $3x^2 + 5x = 8x^3$. To avoid this, remind them about adding like terms, which they accomplished in Chapter 1.

Sharon Testone,
Onondaga Community College

◆ ◆ ◆

Exponent rules are sometimes difficult for students to understand. They forget that to use the product rule, the bases have to be the same; or they forget to use the product rule when there are like bases. This can be said about the quotient rule as well.

Angela Walters,
Capitol College

Section 4.2

When working with scientific notation, students are off by one decimal place or, even worse, they have the wrong sign for the exponent of ten. I always use the example of how mad (or happy) we would be if the bank made a simple error like that (.01 instead of 100 or 1000 instead of 10,000). The small details are very important.

Jane Duncan Nesbit,
Columbia Union College

◆ ◆ ◆

The mental device presented in the text for scientific notation (i.e. based on whether the number is greater than one or less than one) is more straightforward than the traditional rules referring to moving the decimal point to the left or right. But some people confuse "left" and "right." This is a good opportunity to appeal to kinesthetic learners by having them point in the direction that the decimal point is moved.

Rosa Kavanaugh,
Ozarks Technical College

Section 4.3

In my introduction to using letters to represent numbers and the explanation of combining like terms, I tell students that mathematical symbols are like abbreviations. So $3a$ could represent three apples while $2b$ represents two bananas. Thus $3a + 5a = 8a$ means that if we have three apples and buy five more apples we have a total of eight apples. Or $2b + b = 3b$ means that if we have two bananas and buy another banana, we have a total of three bananas. This explanation makes it clear to most students why $3a + 2b$ cannot be combined.

Rosa Kavanaugh,
Ozarks Technical College

◆ ◆ ◆

This section has a lot of new terminology. I give out a vocabulary page with fourteen definitions from this section (monomial, coefficient, like terms etc.) that the students must complete and return to me for credit.

I always include problem #79 from page 341 in the homework assignment.

Tatiana Sviridovsky,
Delaware County Community College

◆ ◆ ◆

I mention to students that it is possible to model real-world phenomena using polynomials and then give them some examples. This helps them to understand the importance of working with polynomials.

When going over the concept of evaluating polynomials, I relate it to our earlier work in evaluating expressions. This helps students to better connect with the idea of evaluating a polynomial.

Angela Walters,
Capitol College

Section 4.4

Remind students of the difference between an equation and an expression. They should also be reminded that the fractions and decimals here cannot be 'cleared'.

Gail G. Burkett,
Palm Beach Community College

Section 4.5

I have them do a binomial times a trinomial before doing the trinomial times the binomial.

Gail G. Burkett,
Palm Beach Community College

◆ ◆ ◆

It has been helpful to my students for me to show the many ways to visualize polynomial multiplication (rectangle area, set up like real number multi-plication and using the distributive property and adding like terms).

Jane Duncan Nesbit,
Columbia Union College

◆ ◆ ◆

I use the FOIL method in this section rather than the method shown in examples # 7 and #8 on pp. 354–355. Most students are familiar with the FOIL method and they become confused with too many ways to do the same problem.

Tatiana Sviridovsky,
Delaware County Community College

◆ ◆ ◆

Never multiply two trinomials horizontally. I would always complete the problem vertically. Students have difficulty when too many terms are involved.

Be sure to emphasize the difference between $x^2 x^3$ and $\left(x^2\right)^3$. I show the first as: $xx\,xxx = x^5$ and the second as $x^2 x^2 x^2 = xx\,xx\,xx = x^6$. I found that students really need to see this "picture" before they understand what is being taught.

Sharon Testone,
Onondaga Community College

Section 4.6

I always insist that the students state the formulas for the special products in words. For example, $a^2 - b^2 = (a - b)(a + b)$ they should say "the difference between the squares of the first and the second term is equal to the difference between these terms multiplied by the sum of these terms". Then in a specific example, they begin by identifying the terms whose squares are given. If the expression to be factored is $64r^2 - 9$, the students have to say: "We look at the squares of $8r$ and 3, so we use the product of their difference and their sum to factor: $(8r - 3)(8r + 3)$".

Tatiana Sviridovsky,
Delaware County Community College

◆ ◆ ◆

I don't emphasize rules for special products. They can just multiply the binomials using the method that they have used for any other binomial. I do point out the result because this will help them with factoring in the next chapter. I also emphasize that $\left(x + 2\right)^2$ means $(x + 2)(x + 2)$ so we should NOT get an answer of $x^2 + 4$. (This saves time!)

Sharon Testone,
Onondaga Community College

◆ ◆ ◆

Students usually understand how to use FOIL, but have trouble remembering when to use the special products formulas. When I use them, I continually explain why I am using a special product formula and that its purpose is to gain speed.

Angela Walters,
Capitol College

Section 4.7

Remind students that it's the details here that count. There's less chance of a mistake if they are neat and don't 'cramp' their work into a small space.

Gail G. Burkett,
Palm Beach Community College

◆ ◆ ◆

Several areas of confusion tend to surface at the end of Chapter 4. Students seem comfortable with $\left(ab^3\right)^2 = a^2b^6$. I believe that this is one reason for so much confusion in squaring binomials. $\left(ab^3\right)^2$ and $\left(a + b^3\right)^2$ appear so much the same to many students that a classroom discussion contrasting the two forms may be helpful.

Students at this stage of the course also tend to confuse $3x + 2(x - 5)$ with $(3x + 2)(x - 5)$. This error often occurs on a final examination. It is helpful to also review the distributive law and address this distinction at this point in the course.

Rosa Kavanaugh,
Ozarks Technical College

Section 4.8

You may want to add some problems with coefficients in the divisor: $\left(6x^2 - x - 17\right) \div (2x + 3)$.

Gail G. Burkett,
Palm Beach Community College

Polynomials: Factoring

SECTION TITLES AND OBJECTIVES

5.1 Introduction to Factoring
Find the greatest common factor, the GCF, of monomials ● Factor polynomials when the terms have a common factor, factoring out the greatest common factor ● Factor certain expressions with four terms using factoring by grouping

5.2 Factoring Trinomials of the Type $x^2 + bx + c$
Factor trinomials of the type $x^2 + bx + c$ by examining the constant term c

5.3 Factoring $ax^2 + bx + c, a \neq 1$: The FOIL Method
Factor trinomials of the type $ax^2 + bx + c, a \neq 1$, using the FOIL method

5.4 Factoring $ax^2 + bx + c, a \neq 1$: The ac-Method
Factor trinomials of the type $ax^2 + bx + c, a \neq 1$, using the *ac*-method

5.5 Factoring Trinomial Squares and Differences of Squares
Recognize trinomial squares ● Factor trinomial squares ● Recognize differences of squares ● Factor differences of squares, being careful to factor completely

5.6 Factoring: A General Strategy
Factor polynomials completely using any of the methods considered in this chapter

5.7 Solving Quadratic Equations by Factoring
Solve equations (already factored) using the principle of zero products ● Solve quadratic equations by factoring and then using the principle of zero products

5.8 Applications of Quadratic Equations
Solve applied problems involving quadratic equations that can be solved by factoring

TEACHING TIPS

I always introduce students to this chapter as being the "reverse" of the previous chapter on multiplying polynomials. For some reason "working backwards" as opposed to learning "factorization" tends to be remembered easier.

Endre Borsos,
Miami-Dade Community College

◆ ◆ ◆

Stress the importance of knowing the basic four operations and where to look in the trinomial for the sign and operation.

Spend a lot of time on applications. Spend time in class helping students set up a variety of problems and leave the solving to them. The hardest part for students is the set-up.

Jane Duncan Nesbit,
Columbia Union College

◆ ◆ ◆

I rearrange the sections in this chapter to present the topics in the order that they are given in the "Factoring Strategy" on Page 443. I identify this **Five Step Factoring Process** by the numbers:

Number 1 is "First always, always, always remove common factors first."
Number 2 is for 2 terms: "Look for difference of squares."
Number 3 is for 3 terms: "Look for a trinomial square; if not, trial and error."
Number 4 is for 4 terms: "Try factoring by grouping."
Number 5 is "Last look to see whether any of the factors can be factored again."

I do not mention the check in this process because I would consider it optional.

Rosa Kavanaugh,
Ozarks Technical College

◆ ◆ ◆

Stress checking the result by multiplying the factored form out and verifying that you get the original problem back.

I find that a majority of my students are already familiar with the quadratic formula and sometimes want to use it before it is introduced in class. I encourage them to use it, but also to try the other methods we are discussing.

Angela Walters,
Capitol College

◆ ◆ ◆

If a graphing calculator is allowed, students can check their work by graphing the original expression and the factored expression to test for some accuracy. It must be noted to students however, that if a problem is factored correctly but not completely, it will appear as the same graph on the calculator.

Roy West,
Robeson Community College

Section 5.1

Remind students that they can check their answers by multiplying (using the distributive property). The only thing that this doesn't check is whether they factored out the largest common factor and not just a common factor.

Jane Duncan Nesbit,
Columbia Union College

◆ ◆ ◆

Students sometimes want to clear fractions before factoring polynomials with fractional coefficients. The confusion seems to increase with a strong, but appropriate, emphasis of clearing fractions in Chapter 2. It is helpful to review that topic at this time and reinforce the difference between factoring an expression $\left(\text{e.g. } \frac{1}{2}x^5 - \frac{1}{4}x^3 + \frac{3}{4}x^2\right)$ and solving a fractional equation $\left(\text{e.g. } \frac{1}{2}x - \frac{1}{4} = \frac{3}{4} + x\right)$.

Rosa Kavanaugh,
Ozarks Technical College

◆ ◆ ◆

After doing a few numeric examples (as done in the text), I find it helpful to do a few examples with several monomials before actually showing a polynomial with two or more terms. This helps students "see" variable factors before looking at polynomials with two or more terms.

Louise Olshan,
County College of Morris

◆ ◆ ◆

In addition to the definition on page 399, I explain that to factor a polynomial means to write

it down in such form that the last operation to do in it is multiplication. This way the students will be able to see why the GCF method cannot be used in $5x^2 + 10x - 7$. If 5 is taken out from the first two terms, the last operation in it is not multiplication: $5(x^2 + 2x) - 7$

When we do examples on taking out the GCF, I emphasize the fact that every term of the polynomial must be divided by the GCF. This way the students understand that the correct answer to $14x + 7 = 7(2x + 1)$, not $7(2x + 0)$.

When factoring by grouping, I have the students write down three main steps.

    Example: $x^3 + x^2 + 2x + 2$:
      Step 1:   Group: $(x^3 + x^2) + (2x + 2)$
      Step 2:   Find the GCF in each group: $x^2(x + 1) + 2(x + 1)$
      Step 3:   Find GCF for both groups: $(x^2 + 2)(x + 1)$

If you compare my approach to how this example is explained on page 403, you may find that it works better for the students. It's all done in three lines with the standard description for each step that will be the same in each grouping problem. Additionally, it helps to avoid the mistake of stopping after the second step. Now, the students understand that the problem needs to be finished.

Tatiana Sviridovsky,
Delaware County Community College

◆ ◆ ◆

I find that students have the most difficulty with factoring by grouping, so I give them many problems to work on in class. I also give them a group project dealing with factoring so they get practice deciding the best method to use.

Angela Walters,
Capitol College

Section 5.2

I do not discuss all the "cases" that are shown in the text. I rather look for two numbers that give the correct product and sum. The signs will need to be correct. I try throughout the course to limit things like "cases", since students begin to think too much in terms of memorization and not of understanding.

Louise Olshan,
County College of Morris

◆ ◆ ◆

In factoring trinomials, check to see if the variables match the pattern that is being studied. When in descending or ascending order, does the middle term have an exponent that is half of the exponent of the variables in the first or third terms?

Roy West,
Robeson Community College

◆ ◆ ◆

When factoring a trinomial, stress trinomials with a coefficient other than 1 in front of the x^2 term. If you spend too much time on problems with a one x^2 coefficient, the students get into the habit of ignoring the coefficient of the x^2 term. I usually skip section 5.2 and go directly into section 5.3.

Annette Wiesner,
University of Wisconsin-Parkside

Section 5.3

In Section 5.3 remember to stress that when completed, no factors should contain a common factor. For example, $(3x + 6)$ has a common factor of 3.

In factoring polynomials of the form $ax^2 + bx + c$ where $a \neq 1$, if the absolute values of the coefficients a, b, and c are close together, then normally (but not always) the factors of a and c that need to be chosen would be close together. This does not always work, but in a world of trial and error this is a good place to start.

Roy West,
Robeson Community College

◆ ◆ ◆

I teach only one method: either the ac-method or the FOIL method of factoring trinomials. I feel that students get too confused trying to learn two methods.

Annette Wiesner,
University of Wisconsin-Parkside

Section 5.4

If students have been successful with the method of section 5.3, they can continue to use that method. However, most of my students need the step-by-step approach of this section. In fact, once they have answered the "product and sum question" correctly, I tell them that they should be successful in factoring the polynomial. I do not teach section 5.3 at all.

Louise Olshan,
County College of Morris

◆ ◆ ◆

I feel that teaching the ac-method is a MUST. It is a wonderful way to factor without random guessing and it makes good use of the factoring by grouping technique. I use it when a does not equal 1.

Some hints to help the students with the ac-method.

a. Remove the GCF. I usually box the GCF and then write the trinomial below it. I tell students that we will save the GCF for the last step, but we don't want it to get in our way now.

b. Once I have the factors that multiply to equal ac and add to equal b, I talk to the students about substitution and why they need to be careful.

   Example: Suppose we have -6 and 2. I would have the students write: $-6 + 2x$.

   I tell them that if there is one negative term, it is easier to factor by grouping if we write the negative term first. However, order does NOT matter. It is just easier if we do it that way.

   Example: Suppose we have -6 and -2. I have the students write this as a sum with the **+** sign circled. $-6x + 2x$ instead of $-6x - 2x$.

   $\left(x^2 - 6x\right) + (-2x + 12)$. This helps with the grouping. Without the circled $+$ sign, the students never know what to do with the second negative sign. They either write:

$$\left(x^2 - 6x\right)(-2x + 12)$$

   which is incorrect or

$$\left(x^2 - 6x\right) - (-2x + 12)$$

   which is incorrect.

c. Finally students often have problems with the last step.

   $x(x - 6) - -2(x - 6)$. They have difficulty seeing that $(x - 6)$ is a common factor.

   So: I show them $x(a) - 2(a)$ and ask them what they would do in this case.

   Then I tell them that (a) could represent $(x - 6)$ and most of them finally see the light.

Sharon Testone,
Onondaga Community College

Section 5.5

Be sure that students recognize perfect squares, especially with variables of powers higher than two. I review this before introducing factoring.

Louise Olshan,
County College of Morris

Section 5.6

When teaching that $x^2 + 9$ does not factor, I begin by asking for the factors. The students will give me $(x + 3)(x + 3)$, $(x + 3)(x - 3)$ and $(x - 3)(x - 3)$. I then multiply each one and show them that none of their answers results in $x^2 + 9$. If I have a very bright group of students, I venture into the realm of imaginary numbers very, very briefly. I show them the correct answer, but tell them that the answer we will be looking for in this course DOES NOT factor in the real number system.

When solving $2(x + 3)(x + 4) = 0$, I have to tell the students NOT to set $2 = 0$. We then discuss why that wouldn't make any sense, but then discuss that it is okay to set x equal to zero if $x(x + 3)(x + 4) = 0$.

Sharon Testone,
Onondaga Community College

◆ ◆ ◆

Remember to stress to students to look for GCF first. As you, the instructor, work problems in class ask the question out loud, "Do we have a GCF?" to get them in the habit of thinking it.

Roy West,
Robeson Community College

Section 5.7

Students frequently make a common mistake when solving quadratic equations using the principle of zero products. When solving an equation like $(x + 2)(x - 3) = 4$ they will try to set each factor on the left to 4 or 1 (since $4 = 4 \cdot 1$). But explain that we are not certain that one factor must be four and the other one. There are infinitely many numbers whose product is four. Setting the quadratic equal to zero needs to be stressed.

Jane Duncan Nesbit,
Columbia Union College

◆ ◆ ◆

When the students learn to solve quadratic equations by factoring there is often a tendency to confuse "factor" with "solve." Some students solve the equation by factoring the trinomial but not setting it equal to zero. Then they cannot proceed to the solutions. Other students instead attempt to "solve" an algebraic expression by setting it equal to zero. Some such errors may be avoided by contrasting the problems "Solve $x^2 - 3x - 4 = 0$" and "Factor $x^2 - 3x - 4$." This is a good time to reinforce the distinction between solving an equation and factoring an expression.

Rosa Kavanaugh,
Ozarks Technical College

◆ ◆ ◆

You can never sufficiently stress the differences in the concepts of factoring a polynomial and solving an equation. After completing this section, I give questions on these two ideas in class, mixing both concepts on a worksheet.

Louise Olshan,
County College of Morris

Section 5.8

In the applications, students tend to confuse the formulas for perimeter and area. It is a valuable use of class time to return to the basic definitions using pictures. It may be helpful to some students to note the word "rim" inside the word "perimeter." If they participate in the construction of the definitions, it will be easier for them to remember the formulas.

Rosa Kavanaugh,
Ozarks Technical College

◆ ◆ ◆

Try to cover all problems in the exercise set for Section 5.8. I usually spend two class periods on word problems.

Deloria Nanze-Davis,
University of Texas, Brownsville, Texas Southmost College

Rational Expressions and Equations

SECTION TITLES AND OBJECTIVES

6.1 Multiplying and Simplifying Rational Expressions
Find all numbers for which a rational expression is not defined ● Multiply a rational expression by 1, using an expression such as A/A ● Simplify rational expressions by factoring the numerator and the denominator and removing factors of 1 ● Multiply rational expressions and simplify

6.2 Division and Reciprocals
Find the reciprocal of a rational expression ● Divide rational expressions and simplify

6.3 Least Common Multiples and Denominators
Find the LCM of several numbers by factoring ● Add fractions, first finding the LCD ● Find the LCM of algebraic expressions by factoring

6.4 Adding Rational Expressions
Add rational expressions

6.5 Subtracting Rational Expressions
Subtract rational expressions ● Simplify combined additions and subtractions of rational expressions

6.6 Solving Rational Equations
Solve rational equations

6.7 Applications Using Rational Equations and Proportions
Solve applied problems using rational equations ● Solve proportion problems

6.8 Complex Rational Expressions
Simplify complex rational expressions

6.9 Direct Variation and Inverse Variation
Find an equation of direct variation given a pair of values of the variables ● Solve applied problems involving direct variation ● Find an equation of inverse variation given a pair of values of the variables ● Solve applied problems involving inverse variation

TEACHING TIPS

Some students have been confused by similarities in the terminology "cross-canceling," "multiplying straight across," and "cross multiplying." This chapter is a good time to clarify the terminology and make the following distinctions:

- "Multiplying straight across" is the way that some people describe multiplication of fractions, that is multiplying the numerators and multiplying the denominators.

- "Cross canceling" is sometimes used to describe the process of simplification by "removing factors of one." It is important to distinguish that this can be done whenever the same factor appears in the numerator **and** denominator of a fraction (or product of fractions.)

- "Cross multiplying" is one way to describe the fact that when one fraction is **equal** to another fraction there is a relationship between the products of the numerator of each and the denominator of the other. A much better way to describe this is the "Principle of Cross Products," as used by Dr. Bittinger. But a number of students arrive using the less precise terminology and need help with clarification.

Rosa Kavanaugh,
Ozarks Technical College

◆ ◆ ◆

Explain to students that we allow the numerator or denominator to be left factored. The purpose of this is that the expression is much more useful in its factored form, especially in graphing the expression.

If a graphing calculator is allowed, students can check their work by graphing the original expression and the simplified expression to test for some accuracy.

Roy West,
Robeson Community College

◆ ◆ ◆

Once you have completed sections 6.4, 6.5, and 6.6, do several nearly identical problems, side-by-side to show students the difference between them.

Solving rational equations vs. Adding/subtracting rational expressions

$$\frac{1}{x} = \frac{1}{8} - \frac{3}{5} \text{ vs. } \frac{1}{x} + \frac{1}{8} - \frac{3}{5}$$

$$\frac{4}{(x-3)} + \frac{2x}{(x^2-9)} = \frac{1}{(x+3)} \text{ vs. } \frac{4}{(x-3)} + \frac{2x}{(x^2-9)} - \frac{1}{(x+3)}$$

Annette Wiesner,
University of Wisconsin-Parkside

Section 6.1

Dr. Bittinger's explanation of canceling on page 488 is very well done. I tell students, "Cancel means divide by common factors." I have found that if I continue to repeat this simple definition throughout the course, it helps to explain the common errors of "illegal canceling" of rational expressions in Chapter 6.

Students have difficulty seeing the difference between dealing with opposites when they simplify a fraction (removing a factor of 1) and finding a common denominator involving opposites. Dr. Bittinger's explanation preceding Example 10 in Section 6.1 is quite good. I sometimes generalize as: "Whenever you have opposites as factors in the numerator and denominator of the same fraction, you can replace that combination by a factor of negative one." Then if a pair of opposites is in the denominators of different fractions being added or subtracted, the common denominator will contain only one of the pair. The other of the pair can be converted to the first by multiplying that fraction by $\frac{(-1)}{(-1)}$.

Rosa Kavanaugh,
Ozarks Technical College

◆ ◆ ◆

I give a rationale for why you would want to create equivalent fractions—"you will need to do this when adding and subtracting rational expressions".

I always use the words "canceling factors" rather than just "canceling" to reinforce what is to be cancelled. This reminds students that numerators and denominators need to be factored before canceling.

Louise Olshan,
County College of Morris

◆ ◆ ◆

For objective (a) be sure to show example #6 on page 490. After spending a lot of

time on factoring in the preceding chapter, the most hard-working students are likely to factor the numerator and cancel $x - 3$.

Keep reminding the students that to reduce the fraction we <u>divide</u> the numerator and denominator by the same number, not just cross the things out. Do example #26 on page 490 and have them compare it to $\frac{5a - 3}{5}$. Explain that crossing out 5 on the top is NOT the same as dividing $5a - 3$ by 5. Also, note that factoring is the survival skill in this chapter.

It's helpful to do multiplication and division of rational expressions on the same day (time permitting).

I always write a set of three rational expressions on the board when working with the -1 rule. I warn the students that exactly two of them can be reduced and let them figure this out.

$$\frac{x - 5}{x + 5}, \frac{x + 5}{5 + x} \text{ and } \frac{x - 5}{5 - x}.$$

It's a short exercise, but at the same time it's a very important summary.

Tatiana Sviridovsky,
Delaware County Community College

Section 6.4

In Section 6.4, the author talks about the missing factor. Explain that this comes from division. To see how many times the denominator will go into the LCD, we divide. The result will always be whatever is missing from the factored forms.

Roy West,
Robeson Community College

Section 6.5

Students have trouble subtracting rational expressions because they do not distribute the negative sign appropriately. They especially have trouble if one denominator is the opposite of the other.

Example: $\dfrac{5}{6} - \dfrac{6}{-x}$

There are many ways to approach this problem, but often it helps to demonstrate that $\frac{-1}{2} = \frac{1}{-2} = -\frac{1}{2}$ and then students can just bring the negative sign to the fraction bar.

$$\frac{5}{x} - \frac{6}{-x} = \frac{5}{x} - \left(-\frac{6}{x}\right) = \frac{5}{x} + \frac{6}{x} = \frac{11}{x}$$

Sharon Testone,
Onondaga Community College

◆ ◆ ◆

In subtraction of polynomial expressions, if students are having difficulty with distributing the negative sign correctly, there is a possible alternative. Make each subtraction problem an addition problem by changing the sign in the numerator or denominator of the fraction being subtracted.

Roy West,
Robeson Community College

Section 6.6

If students have learned to clear fractions when solving fractional equations, they often want to also clear fractions when simplifying rational expressions. Dr. Bittinger does a good job of addressing this issue in the Study Tip "Are You Calculating or Solving?" on page 525 of the text. Another form of the question might be, "Will you keep fractions or clear fractions?"

Rosa Kavanaugh,
Ozarks Technical College

◆ ◆ ◆

I always use the words "multiply both sides of the equation by the LCM" to hopefully reinforce the idea that you can only multiply when you have an equation. I have my students say these words with me.

Students need to be reminded of the need to check or verify their potential answers. I require that students give the domain for the expressions in the equation and then verify whether a "potential solution" is an actual solution.

Louise Olshan,
County College of Morris

Section 6.7

I often do some of the "work" problems by stating "the work the first person/machine does in one hour plus the work that the second person/machine does in one hour equals the work that they do together in one hour". Then, I form the equation that needs to be solved. After students are comfortable with one hour, you can do other problems where two or more hours are involved.

Louise Olshan,
County College of Morris

Section 6.8

I try to use just method one. I find showing both methods one and two leads to confusion.

Louise Olshan,
County College of Morris

◆ ◆ ◆

With complex fractions, I think method two in the text works the best. This way, students are just using concepts that they know. They are combining the fractions in the numerator and fractions in the denominator. Finally, they are multiplying the numerator by the reciprocal of the denominator. Students have trouble clearing fractions as required in method one.

Sharon Testone,
Onondaga Community College

7 Systems of Equations

SECTION TITLES AND OBJECTIVES

7.1 Systems of Equations in Two Variables
Determine whether an ordered pair is a solution of a system of equations ● Solve systems of two linear equations in two variables by graphing

7.2 The Substitution Method
Solve a system of two equations in two variables by the substitution method when one of the equations has a variable alone on one side ● Solve a system of two equations in two variables by the substitution method when neither equation has a variable alone on one side ● Solve applied problems by translating to a system of two equations and then solving using the substitution method

7.3 The Elimination Method
Solve a system of two equations in two variables using the elimination method when no multiplication is necessary ● Solve a system of two equations in two variables using the elimination method when multiplication is necessary

7.4 Applications and Problem Solving
Solve applied problems by translating to a system of two equations in two variables

7.5 Applications with Motion
Solve motion problems using the formula $d = rt$

TEACHING TIPS

When introducing systems of equations, I begin by graphing two equations on the same coordinate plane. This leads nicely to solving by graphing. I then use these examples to show another way to solve the problem by using either elimination or substitution. I tell students that they should use the easiest method when solving. They should choose elimination if both variables are on the same side in both equations. They should choose substitution if one of the equations is solved for one of the variables.

A hint that I give when solving substitution problems is to put ( ) in for the variable before substituting. This method helps them to remember to distribute a negative sign.

Example:

$$x - y = 6$$
$$y = 3x + 4$$
$$x - (\ ) = 6$$

then substitute $3x + 4$.

A hint that I give for solving elimination problems when both equations need to be transformed is to multiply each equation by the coefficient of the variable from the other equation. Of course, I mention the need for the terms to be "opposites".

Example:

$$2x + 5y = 6$$
$$3x - 4y = 10$$

The first equation could be multiplied by 3 and the second by -2 or the first equation could be multiplied by 4 and the second by 5. I point out why there is no need to multiply by a negative number in the second option.

Sharon Testone,
Onondaga Community College

◆ ◆ ◆

I tell students that when solving a system by graphing, their answer may be an estimate. All examples in the text come out to be exact.

Have a discussion in class to discover how many solutions are possible. Ask the question, "In how many ways can two lines cross, if ever?"

Roy West,
Robeson Community College

◆ ◆ ◆

Stress that the solution of a system of equations is the point of intersection of two lines. Always have the students write the solution in "ordered pair" form. This helps in explaining inconsistent and dependent solutions. If we get a false equation (inconsistent), there is no point of intersection. Therefore, the lines are parallel. If we get an equation that is true for all values of the variable (dependent), then the lines intersect at more than one point or they are the same line.

Annette Wiesner,
University of Wisconsin-Parkside

Section 7.1

When solving a system graphically it is helpful to emphasize to students that there are two different lines representing two different equations by writing and graphing each in a different color (either using colored chalk, dry erase markers, or transparency pens) or different type lines on the graphing calculator.

Rosa Kavanaugh,
Ozarks Technical College

◆ ◆ ◆

I stress that a graph is a "picture" of the solutions of one equation with two variables. Then, I introduce a system with two equations with two variables and look at the graphs of each equation.

Discuss the inaccuracy of depending on a graph for finding the solution.

I do not let my students give answers like "parallel lines" or "coincident lines". I try to stress that the solution, if one exists, should be an ordered pair or an equation that generates all the ordered pairs that are solutions, in the case of coincident lines.

Louise Olshan,
County College of Morris

◆ ◆ ◆

When you work on objective (a), use the following example:
Determine whether the given ordered pair is a solution of the system of equations

$$2x + 3y = 12$$
$$x - 4y = -5$$

a) $(1, 2)$, b) $(6, 0)$, c) $(3, 2)$

For both (a) and (b) the answer is "no" but $(6, 0)$ works in the first equation, and this will illustrate the importance of testing the given pair in both equations.

When you teach this section, review the variety of the methods used to graph the straight line.

Usually after this section you will cover the substitution and the elimination methods. Make students think what are the advantages and disadvantages of the graphing method. The advantage is that it helps to visualize the concept of the inconsistent and consistent dependent systems. The disadvantage is that it's sometimes difficult to get the exact answer, especially if it contains non-integer values.

Tatiana Sviridovsky,
Delaware County Community College

Section 7.2

I tell students to avoid substitution, if there is no variable with a coefficient of 1 or −1.

Louise Olshan,
County College of Morris

Section 7.3

Stress that different multipliers can all be correct.

Louise Olshan,
County College of Morris

◆ ◆ ◆

In using the elimination method, show how to avoid fractions in finding the second variable if the first variable is found to be a fraction. Instead of substituting the variable you found first to find the second, start back from the beginning and eliminate the variable you found.

Roy West,
Robeson Community College

Section 7.5

The acronym "dirt" helps some students to remember the formula "$d = r \cdot t$" for "distance is rate multiplied by time."

Rosa Kavanaugh,
Ozarks Technical College

8 Radical Expressions and Equations

SECTION TITLES AND OBJECTIVES

8.1   Introduction to Radical Expressions
Find the principal square roots and their opposites of the whole numbers from 0^2 to 25^2 • Approximate square roots of real numbers using a calculator • Solve applied problems involving square roots • Identify radicands of radical expressions • Determine whether a radical expression represents a real number • Simplify a radical expression with a perfect-square radicand

8.2   Multiplying and Simplifying with Radical Expressions
Simplify radical expressions • Simplify radical expressions where radicands are powers • Multiply radical expressions and, if possible, simplify.

8.3   Quotients Involving Radical Expressions
Divide radical expressions • Simplify square roots of quotients • Rationalize the denominator of a radical expression

8.4   Addition, Subtraction, and More Multiplication
Add or subtract with radical notation, using the distributive law to simplify • Multiply expressions involving radicals, where some of the expressions contain more than one term • Rationalize denominators having two terms

8.5   Radical Equations
Solve radical equations with one or two radical terms isolated, using the principle of squaring once • Solve radical equations with two radical terms, using the principle of squaring twice • Solve applied problems using radical equations

8.6   Applications with Right Triangles
Given the lengths of any two sides of a right triangle, find the length of the third side • Solve applied problems involving right triangles

TEACHING TIPS

I believe that students connect more meaning with radicals if they are encouraged to do some decimal approximations before they consult their calculators. When asking for an approximation of $\sqrt{38}$, I would ask the students to approximate **before** they perform the operations on their calculators. With a little direction, they usually predict an answer between 6.1 and 6.3. This helps them to develop some number sense.

Students believe that $\sqrt{25 + 64} = \sqrt{25} + \sqrt{64}$. You need to show them why this is not true.

Sharon Testone,
Onondaga Community College

◆ ◆ ◆

Caution students that x cannot be canceled in this expression

$$\frac{4\sqrt{xy}}{x}$$

but it can be canceled in the expression

$$\frac{4x\sqrt{5y}}{x}.$$

Roy West,
Robeson Community College

◆ ◆ ◆

Students at this level have a hard time "seeing" a perfect square factor in a number. It is best to have students find the prime factorization of the radicand and then look for "pairs" of factors when simplifying. For example, write:

$$\sqrt{48} = \sqrt{(2 \cdot 2 \cdot 2 \cdot 2 \cdot 3)}$$

instead of

$$\sqrt{48} = \sqrt{(16 \cdot 3)}.$$

The prime factorization method helps students make a smooth transition to simplifying other roots: for cube root look for "three identical factors," for fourth root look for "four identical factors," and so on.

Annette Wiesner,
University of Wisconsin-Parkside

Section 8.1

Students should not use the words "radical 25" or "root of 25", rather "square root of 25", looking to the future in another class where they must work with other indices. I mention the word index, again preparing for a future course.

I make note of the fact that needing a non-negative radicand is not true when working with an odd-number index.

Louise Olshan,
County College of Morris

◆ ◆ ◆

For objective (a), don't just put examples on the board. Ask the students to open the book and compare the instructions to problems #1–10 and #11–20 on page 633. It may help the visual learners to remember the difference between finding the square roots and finding the principal square root.

Tatiana Sviridovsky,
Delaware County Community College

Section 8.2

Show students that the rules for multiplying radicals and simplifying radicals are really the same rule in different directions.

Be sure students are aware of the difference of multiplying 5 times $\sqrt{3}$ and multiplying $\sqrt{5}$ times $\sqrt{3}$.

Louise Olshan,
County College of Morris

Section 8.3

After the rules on pp. 636 and 644 are covered, you may want to remind the students that there is no similar rule that can be applied to $\sqrt{a + b}$. A good example is: $\sqrt{64 + 36} = 10$ but $\sqrt{64} + \sqrt{36} = 14$.

Tatiana Sviridovsky,
Delaware County Community College

Section 8.4

Tell students to simplify radicals first, before rationalizing the denominator to be consistent with the idea of simplifying before adding or subtracting radicals.

Louise Olshan,
County College of Morris

◆ ◆ ◆

It's very helpful to do a multiplication problem with the conjugates and then to use the same conjugates in the denominators to be rationalized. Don't use the conjugates whose product is a negative number in the beginning examples.

Good sequence of problems:

1. Multiply $\left(\sqrt{6} - 2\right)\left(\sqrt{6} + 2\right)$.

2. Rationalize the denominator: $\dfrac{3}{\sqrt{6} - 2}$.

> Tatiana Sviridovsky,
> *Delaware County Community College*

♦ ♦ ♦

Students always have problems ration-alizing denominators. They have difficulty distinguishing between the following types of problems.

Example: Rationalize $\dfrac{3}{\sqrt{x + 5}}$ vs. Rationalize $\dfrac{3}{\sqrt{x} + 5}$

I try to distinguish between the two by saying the operation sign is "trapped" and has to remain or it is "free" and it has to change.

> Sharon Testone,
> *Onondaga Community College*

Section 8.5

Correctly squaring the binomials involved is probably the most common difficulty that students have with solving equations with radicals. It is tempting to encourage them to write the factors twice and then use the FOIL method. This is not helpful to students in the long run. Almost all of them are continuing to a higher-level mathematics course. Continuing to use this step is a crutch that hinders them as they attempt to progress. I tell them that they are not ready for the next course unless they can square the binomial by inspection.

> Rosa Kavanaugh,
> *Ozarks Technical College*

♦ ♦ ♦

If graphing calculators are allowed in your class, they will help the students to understand the concept of the extraneous roots.

> Tatiana Sviridovsky,
> *Delaware County Community College*

Section 8.6

It's optional, but to brighten up the course and to give your students a few bonus points, you can assign research/presentations on the life and discoveries of Pythagoras.

> Tatiana Sviridovsky,
> *Delaware County Community College*

9 Quadratic Equations

TEACHING TIPS

Remind students that we have previously stated that in any equation we can divide both sides by any non-zero number and not change the solutions. However, dividing both sides by x is not allowed since x can take on any value, including 0.

Roy West,
Robeson Community College

Section 9.1

Relate this section to section 5.7 where quadratic equations are solved by factoring.

Louise Olshan,
County College of Morris

◆ ◆ ◆

You don't need too many examples from objective (a) but you definitely need one with the coefficients of -1 and 0 (which are included in the text): $-x^2 + 4x = 0$;

A good strategy is to reduce all coefficients where possible. For example, in problem #41 on page 692 the coefficients can be divided by 2. Show this to the students.

Tatiana Sviridovsky,
Delaware County Community College

Section 9.2

Stress the need for the "$\pm$" square root. I downplay using the $ax^2 + c = 0$ as a special case.

Louise Olshan,
County College of Morris

◆ ◆ ◆

If you teach completing the square, then use the fact that, for an equation in the form of $y = a(x - h)^2 + k$, the vertix is (h, k). It is usually best to build on something the students already know. If you don't teach completing the square, then use

$$\left(\frac{-b}{2a}, f\left(\frac{-b}{2a}\right)\right).$$

Annette Wiesner,
University of Wisconsin-Parkside

Section 9.3

Be sure to emphasize the numerator in the Quadratic formula:

$$x = \frac{-b \pm \sqrt{b^2 - 4ac}}{2a}.$$

I have students write the formula repeatedly in class when they are learning it.

Louise Olshan,
County College of Morris

◆ ◆ ◆

Usually my first example has a positive b; therefore, $-b$ in the formula is a negative number. Then I do an example with negative b and remind the students that the negative sign used with the variable tells us to use the opposite value to what's given which is not necessarily a negative number.

It's very difficult to get a perfectly simplified irrational answer in a quadratic equation from a student. Many of them are ready to reduce

$$\frac{4 + \sqrt{6}}{2}$$

at the same time when another part of your class doesn't see how to reduce

$$\frac{4 + 6\sqrt{5}}{2}.$$

I tell them to use the "gas mask strategy":

It means they must circle three numbers: the denominator (2), the number to the left of the plus/minus sign (4) and the number to the right of plus/minus sign, but NOT in the radicand (6). If all three of them have a common factor, we divide each of them by this factor:

$$\frac{4 + 6\sqrt{5}}{2} = \frac{2 + 3\sqrt{5}}{1} = 2 + 3\sqrt{5}.$$

I certainly explain in class that this is just a strategy and this step is justified by what we've learned in the chapter on rational expressions.

In examples like problem #34 on page 708 (irrational answers), show the students that as we do the check for extraneous roots, it's easier to find the numbers that cannot be used as the answers to this equation (0 and -6) and to compare them to the actual answers than to test the actual irrational answers to make sure that they are not extraneous.

Tatiana Sviridovsky,
Delaware County Community College

Students often write the formula without extending the fraction bar under the $-b$. I am always saying "$-b$ plus or minus the square root of b squared minus $4ac$ ALL OVER $2a$."

When using the quadratic formula, students often forget to put the trinomial in descending order.

Sharon Testone,
Onondaga Community College

◆ ◆ ◆

In Section 9.3, state that we have built a machine that basically does all of completing the square. It is the quadratic formula and it gives us the solutions in one step. However, those solutions need to be simplified, which will take more steps.

Roy West,
Robeson Community College

Section 9.4

Dr. Bittinger includes a nice caution following Example 2 of Section 9.4. This situation is analogous to providing a definition in another subject area. For example, in biology, we do not use the word "photosynthesis" in a definition of "photosynthesis." A dictionary does not use a word in its own definition. Likewise in algebra, $x = 3x + 8$ is not a solution to an equation. This is not troublesome to most students, but becomes much more of an issue in solving a formula such as $AB = AC + BC$ for B.

The other difficulty that students tend to have here is remembering to factor. I refer them to the "Equation Solving Procedure" in Section 2.3 and recommend that they write an addendum to step 6: "In order to factor in a formula, it may be necessary to know what to factor by."

Rosa Kavanaugh,
Ozarks Technical College

Section 9.6

I do not introduce symmetry until we have graphed several quadratic functions rather than the first idea as in the text.

Louise Olshan,
County College of Morris

Section 9.7

Students have difficulty understanding the difference between a function and a relation. This needs to be demonstrated in words, graphs, and pictures.

Sharon Testone,
Onondaga Community College

INDEX OF STUDY TIPS

With page references to Bittinger's Introductory Algebra, *Eleventh Edition*

To the Instructor:

The study tips that follow can be used in a variety of ways other than in the order they arise in the books. Admittedly, we would like all students to have mastered these skills before they start our courses, but this is often not the case.

One way to use these study tips is by category. For example, when you are about to give a test, review all the tips on test taking with your students. When you sense that students are not using their time wisely, you might cover all the suggestions on time management. Keep in mind that each tip may not work for each student, but certainly every student will gain something from these suggestions. Good luck!

Study Tips by Chapter, Section, and Page Number

Transparency Masters

Test Aid: Number Lines

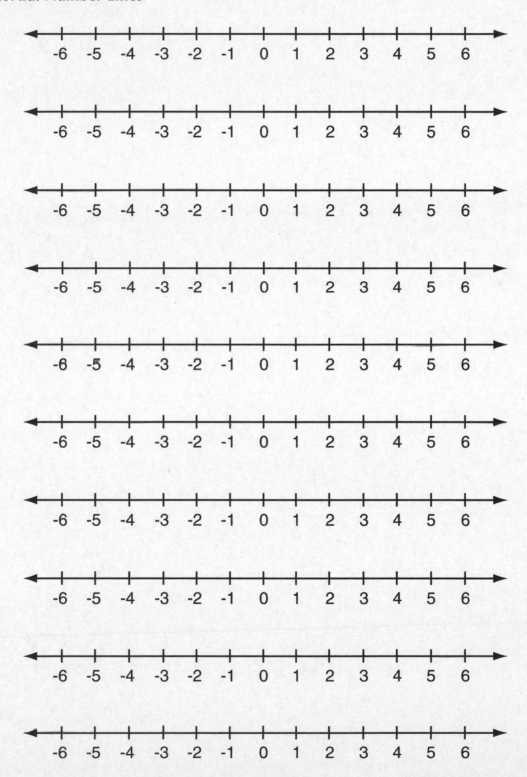

Transparency Master: Number Lines

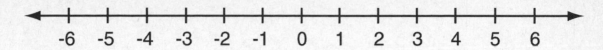

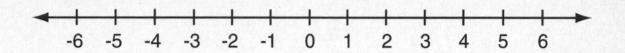

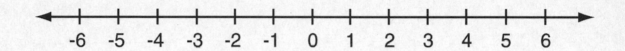

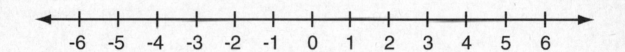

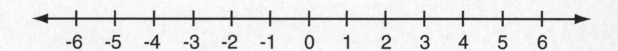

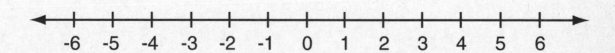

Test Aid: Rectangular Coordinate Grids

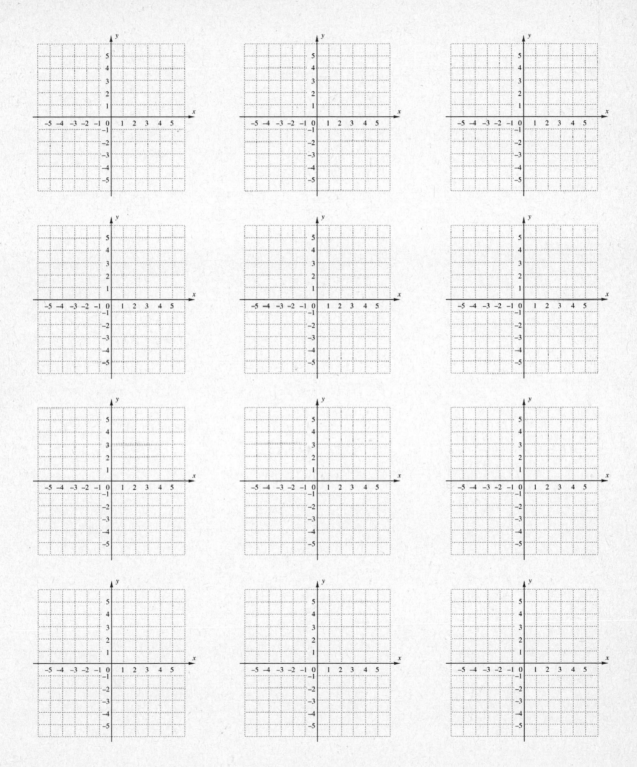

Test Aid: Rectangular Coordinate Grids

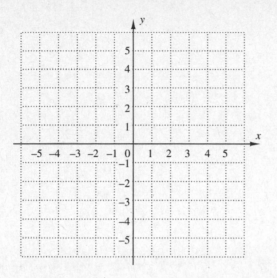

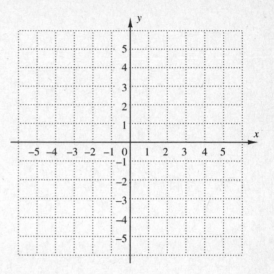

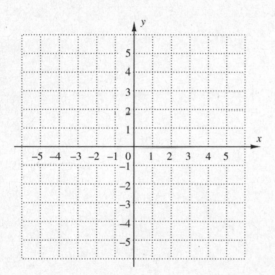

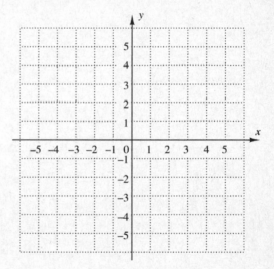

Transparency Master: Rectangular Coordinate Grid

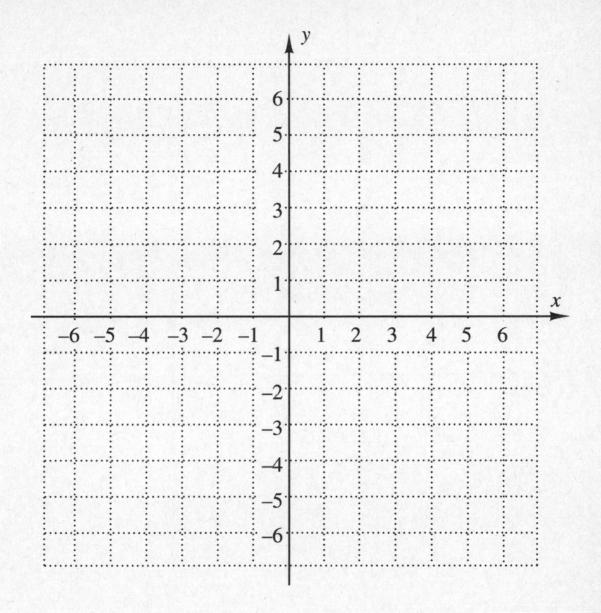

LIST OF AVAILABLE SUPPLEMENTS

Student Supplements	Instructor Supplements
Worksheets for Classroom or Lab practice (ISBN: 978-0-321-64073-4)	**Annotated Instructor's Edition** (ISBN: 978-0-321-62897-8)

Worksheets for Classroom or Lab practice
(ISBN: 978-0-321-64073-4)
These classroom- and lab-friendly workbooks offer the following resources for every section of the text: a list of learning objectives, vocabulary practice problems, and extra practice exercises with ample work space.

Student's Solutions Manual
(ISBN: 978-0-321-64070-3)
By Judith Penna

Contains completely worked-out annotated solutions for all the odd-numbered exercises in the text. Also includes fully worked-out annotated solutions for all the exercises (odd- and even-numbered) in the Mid-Chapter Reviews, the Summary and Reviews, the Chapter Tests, and the Cumulative Reviews.

Chapter Test Prep Videos
Chapter Tests can serve as practice tests to help you study. Watch instructors work through step-by-step solutions to all the Chapter Test exercises from the textbook. Chapter Test Prep videos are available on YouTube (search using BittingerIntroAlg) and in MyMathLab. They are also included on the Video Resources on DVD described below and available for purchase at www.MyPearsonStore.com.

Video Resources on DVD Featuring Chapter Test Prep Videos (ISBN: 978-0-321-64075-8)
- Complete set of lectures covering every objective of every section in the textbook
- Complete set of Chapter Test Prep videos (see above)
- All video include optional English and Spanish subtitles.
- Ideal for distance learning or supplemental instruction
- DVD-ROM format for student use at home or on campus

Annotated Instructor's Edition
(ISBN: 978-0-321-62897-8)
Includes answers to all exercises printed in blue on the same page as the exercises. Also includes the student answer section, for easy reference.

Instructor's Solutions Manual
(ISBN: 978-0-321-64068-0)
By Judith Penna

Contains brief solutions to the even-numbered exercises in the exercise sets. Also includes fully worked-out annotated solutions for all the exercises (odd- and even-numbered) in the Mid-Chapter Reviews, the Summary and Reviews, the Chapter Tests, and the Cumulative Reviews.

Printed Test Forms (ISBN: 978-0-321-64067-3)
By Laurie Hurley
- Contains one diagnostic test and one pretest for each chapter.
- **New!** Includes two versions of a short mid-chapter quiz.
- Provides eight test forms for every chapter and eight test forms for the final exam.
- For the chapter tests, four free-response tests are modeled after the chapter tests in the main text, two tests are designed for 50-minute class periods and organized so that each objective in the chapter is covered on one of the tests, and two tests consist of multiple-choice questions. Chapter texts also include more challenging Synthesis questions.
- For the final exam, three test forms are organized by chapter, three forms are organized by question type, and two forms are multiple-choice tests.

Student Supplements	Instructor Supplements
InterAct Math Tutorial Website (www.interactmath.com) Get practice and tutorial help online! This interactive tutorial website provides algorithmically generated practice exercises that correlate directly to the exercises in the textbook. Students can retry an exercise as many times as they like with new values each time for unlimited practice and mastery. Every exercise is accompanied by an interactive guided solution that provides helpful feedback for incorrect answers, and students can also view a worked-out sample problem that steps them through an exercise similar to the one they're working on.	**Instructor's Resource Manual** (ISBN: 978-0-321-64070-0) • Features resources and teaching tips designed to help both new and adjunct faculty with course preparation and classroom management. • **New!** Includes a mini-lecture for each section of the text with objectives, key examples, and teaching tips. • Additional resources include general first-time advice, sample syllabi, teaching tips, collaborative learning activities, correlation guide, video index, and transparency masters.
MathXL® Tutorials on CD (ISBN: 978-0-321-64064-2) This interactive tutorial CD-ROM provides algorithmically generated practice exercises that are correlated at the objective level to the exercises in the textbook. Every practice exercise is accompanied by an example and a guided solution designed to involve students in the solution process. Selected exercises may also include a video clip to help students visualize concepts. The software provides helpful feedback for incorrect answers and can generate printed summaries of students' progress.	

Additional Media Supplements

MyMathLab **MyMathLab® Online Course (access code required)**

MyMathLab is a series of text-specific, easily customizable online courses for Pearson Education's textbooks in mathematics and statistics. Powered by CourseCompass™ (our online teaching and learning environment) and MathXL™ (our online homework, tutorial, and assessment system), MyMathLab gives instructors the tools they need to deliver all or a portion of their course online, whether their students are in a lab setting or working from home. MyMathLab provides a rich and flexible set of course materials, featuring free-response exercises that are algorithmically generated for unlimited practice and mastery. Students can also use online tools, such as video lectures, animations, interactive math games, and a multimedia textbook, to independently improve their understanding and performance. Instructors can use MyMathLab's homework and test managers to select and assign online exercises correlated directly to the textbook, and they can also create and assign their own online exercises and import TestGen tests for added flexibility. MyMathLab's online gradebook—designed specifically for mathematics and statistics—automatically tracks students' homework and test results and gives the instructor control over how to calculate final grades. Instructors can also add offline (paper-and-pencil) grades to the gradebook. MyMathLab also includes access to the **Pearson Tutor Center** (www.pearsontutorservices.com). The Tutor Center is staffed by qualified mathematics instructors who provide textbook-specific tutoring for students via toll-free phone, fax, email, and interactive Web sessions. MyMathLab is available to qualified adopters. For more information, visit our website at www.mymathlab.com or contact your sales representative.

MathXL **MathXL® Online Course (access code required)**

MathXL® is a powerful online homework, tutorial, and assessment system that accompanies Pearson Education's textbooks in mathematics or statistics.

With MathXL, instructors can

- create, edit, and assign online homework and tests using algorithmically generated exercises correlated at the objective level to the textbook.
- create and assign their own online exercises and import TestGen tests for added flexibility.
- maintain records of all student work tracked in MathXL's online gradebook.

With MathXL, students can

- take chapter tests in MathXL and receive personalized study plans based on their test results.
- use the study plan to link directly to tutorial exercises for the objectives they need to study and retest.
- access supplemental animations and video clips directly from selected exercises.

MathXL is available to qualified adopters. For more information, visit our website at www.mathxl.com, or contact your Pearson sales representative.

TestGen® (www.pearsoned.com/testgen) enables instructors to build, edit, and print tests using a computerized bank of questions developed to cover all the objectives of the text. TestGen is algorithmically based, allowing instructors to create multiple but equivalent versions of the same questions or test with the click of a button. Instructors can also modify test bank questions or add new questions. The software and test bank are available for download from Pearson Education's online catalog.

PowerPoint® Lecture Slides present key concepts and definitions from the text. Slides are available to download from within MyMathlab and from Pearson Education's online catalog.

Pearson Math Adjunct Support Center (http://www.pearsontutorservices.com/math-adjunct.html) is staffed by qualified instructors with more than 100 years of combined experience at both the community college and university levels. Assistance is provided for faculty in the following areas: suggested syllabus consultation, tips on using materials packed with your book, book-specific content assistance, and teaching suggestions, including advice on classroom strategies.

Getting Started with MathXL

Overview

MathXL is a powerful online homework, tutorial, and assessment system tied to Pearson textbooks in Mathematics and Statistics. Ideal for use in a lecture, self-paced, or distance-learning course, MathXL diagnoses students' weaknesses and creates a personalized study plan based on their test results. MathXL provides students with unlimited practice using a database of algorithmically generated exercises correlated to the exercises in their textbook. Each tutorial exercise is accompanied by an interactive guided solution and a sample problem to help students improve their skills independently. Instructors can use MathXL to create online homework assignments, quizzes, and tests that are automatically graded and tracked. Instructors can view and manage all students' homework and test results, study pains, and tutorial work in MathXL's flexible online gradebook.

How to Adopt MathXL

1. **Getting Access**

   If you are interested in using MathXL for one or more of your courses, contact your Pearson Education sales representative to request access to *MathXL.* (If you are not sure who your sales representative is, go to http://www.pearsonhighered.com/educator/replocator/.)

2. **Registering**

   Registering is an easy process that takes only a few minutes, and you need to register only once, even if you are teaching more than one course with MathXL. As part of the registration process, you select a login name and password that you will use from then on to access your MathXL course. Once you have your instructor access code, go to www.mathxl.com, click the **Register** button, and follow the on-screen instructions to register and log in.

3. **Creating Your MathXL Course**

   Once you've registered, creating your MathXL course is easy! Simply log in at www.mathxl.com, go to the Course Manager, and click "Create or copy a course". You will be asked to select the textbook you are using and enter some very basic information about your course. You can create as many courses as you need, and you can customize course coverage to match your syllabus if you wish.

4. **Ordering Books for Your Students**

   To access your MathXL course, each student needs to register in MathXL using a student access code, and then register in your course with your CourseID. The easiest way to supply your students with access codes is to order your textbook packaged with the *MathXL Student Access Kit.* Visit the **Books Available** section of the website at www.mathxl.com for a complete list of package ISBNs. The system will generate a course ID when you create your course.

How to Learn More about MathXL

- To learn more about MathXL, visit our website at www.mathxl.com, or contact your Pearson Education sales representative to schedule a demonstration.
- For detailed instructions on how to register, log in, and set up your first MathXL course, visit the **Getting Started** section of the MathXL website at www.mathxl.com.

Getting Started with MyMathLab™

Overview

MyMathLab is a series of text-specific online courses that accompany Pearson Education textbooks in Mathematics and Statistics. Since 2001, MyMathLab has helped over 5 million students succeed at math at more than 1850 colleges and universities. Students and educators alike have benefited from MyMathLab's dependable and easy-to-use online homework, tests, guided solutions, multimedia, ebooks, study plan and tutorial exercises. Pearson's service teams provide training and support when you need it, and MyMathLab offers the broadest range of titles available for adoption.

When you adopt the MyMathLab course for your textbook, your students can view the textbook pages in electronic from and link to supplemental multimedia resources—such as animations and video clips—directly from the eBook. MyMathLab provides students with algorithmically generated tutorial exercises correlated to the exercises in their text, and the system generates individualized study plans based on student test results. MyMathLab's powerful homework and test managers and flexible online gradebook make it easy for instructors to create and manage online assignments that are automatically graded, so they can spend less time grading and more time teaching!

How to Adopt MyMathLab

1. **Getting Access**
   If you are interested in using MyMathLab for one or more of your courses, contact your Pearson Education sales representative to request access to *MyMathLab*. (If you are not sure who your sales representative is, go to http://www.pearsonhighered.com/educator/replocator/.)

2. **Registering**
   MyMathLab courses are accessed through an online learning environment called CourseCompass, so to adopt a MyMathLab course, you need to register in CourseCompass. Registering is an easy process that takes only a few minutes, and you need to register only once, even if you are teaching more than one MyMathLab course. As part of the registration process, you select a login name and password that you will use from then on to access your MyMathLab course. Once you have your instructor access code, go to www.coursecompass.com, click the **Register** button for educators, and follow the on-screen instructions to register and log in.

3. **Creating Your MyMathLab Course**
   Once you've registered in CourseCompass, creating your MyMathLab course is easy. You will simply be asked to select the course materials for your textbook and enter some very basic information about your course. Approximately one business day later (and often after only a few minutes), you will be notified via e-mail that your course is ready, and you will then be able to log in and begin exploring MyMathLab.

4. **Ordering Books for Your Students**
   To access your MyMathLab course, each student needs to register in CourseCompass using a student access code and register in your course with a CourseID. The easiest way to supply your students with access codes is to order your textbook packaged with the *MyMathLab Student Access Kit*. Visit the **Titles Available** section of the website www.mymathlab.com for a complete list of package ISBNs. The system will generate a course ID when you create your course.

How to Learn More about MyMathLab
- To learn more about MyMathLab, visit our website at www.mymathlab, or contact your Pearson Education sales representative to schedule a demonstration.
- For detailed instructions on how to register, log in, and set up your first MyMathLab course, visit the **Getting Started** section of the MyMathLab website at www.mymathlab.com.

Helpful Tips for Using Supplements and Technology

Endre Borsos,
Miami-Dade Community College

- TestGen is a lot of help in constructing tests for every instructor. For students who miss class or need more time comprehending the material the video series is a tremendous addition to the book.

Gail Burkett, *Palm Beach Community College*

- I use TestGen for all my tests and quizzes. For each chapter test, I make several versions to avoid any cheating problems. I can say I have found TestGen to be easy to use, well stocked with questions and consistent with the textbook.

- MyMathLab is an integral part of our course. Homework can be turned in online or by the traditional paper method. Numerous students have thanked me for the online homework option. Many have said they find the extra practice available and the guidance the tutorial provides to be invaluable. We have a mandatory lab assignment for each section, consisting of 5 or 6 questions. Students are able to get help online, to find more practice, and to get tutoring and review. Several of my colleagues give quizzes online. In general, faculty and student feedback for MyMathLab has been very positive.

- I have found the Videos are a good backup for the absent student or very visual learner. I like giving the students several options.

Jane Duncan Nesbit, *Columbia Union College*

- I loan the videos to students who missed a class or who need additional help mastering a particular concept. All of these supplements are encouraged but not required.

Rosa Kavanaugh,
Ozarks Technical College

- The videos are probably the resource that our students use most. We suggest that students who have to miss class view the videos to try to replace the classroom explanations that they missed.

- The students who especially appreciate the videos are those who simply can't grasp all of the concepts with the first explanation and need another version. We find a number of students in this course enter with absolutely no background in algebra. When we cover in one semester a course that is presented over a period of one year in high school, we find that the pace is almost overwhelming for many students. They appreciate the opportunity to watch the videos, stop and replay particularly difficult portions, and then watch them again, if necessary.

- One special way that we have suggested that students use the videos is to watch the video until the instructor presents a problem that he/she plans to work as an example. We recommend that the student copy the problem and pause the video at that point. Then the student can work the problem at his/her own pace. When the problem is completed or the student has reached an impasse, he/she can start the video again and check the work. The instructor's explanation of the problem will provide the student with feedback on his/her work.

Deloria Nanze-Davis, *University of Texas, Brownsville, Texas Southmost College*

- I encourage the students to check out the videos.

Louise Olshan, *County College of Morris*

- Over the years, many students made use of the Videos that were correlated with our textbook. The Videos were available in the Math Center and in the Learning Resource Center, where they could even be taken out overnight. Students now find the CDs provided to be very helpful. Often a student will use the CD when they have missed a class or when they are struggling with some concept.

■ I have made all my assignments available to students in MyMathLab. Students can use MyMathLab at any time when they are having difficulty. I stress using the "Help Me Solve This" and "View an Example" buttons. Doing assignments at MyMathLab gives students much needed "drill and practice" with excellent resources for help. In the past I have taken my class to the Math Center Lab occasionally to work on an assignment using MyMathLab so that they can see all the wonderful help that is available.

■ In another (non-remedial) class, I have created quizzes at MyMathLab that students must take before the class test. This prepares them for the class test by showing them what they need to study for the class test.

Tatiana Sviridovsky, *Delaware County Community College*

■ I use TestGen a lot. However, I use it for ungraded work more frequently than for actual tests. One of the reasons is that because it also creates the answer key, it's a quick way to prepare a review handout/sample test for the students. The other reason is that in some chapters students just try to plug in the answers from the choices without solving the problems (this applies to Chapter 2 equations, systems of linear equations, and to some of the factoring problems). For most problems in the TestGen exams I require the students to show their work, and don't give them credit otherwise.

■ As for MyMathLab, I usually take time during the very first class meeting to go online in class and show the students what MyMathLab has to offer. I remind them that the Videos are especially helpful if they missed a class or a review for a chapter test and may want to see the material (at least a part of the chapter) covered again. Time permitting, I take them to the computer lab several times during the semester and we do interactive practice or group activities.

Sharon Testone, *Onondaga Community College*

■ I teach both in the classroom and on-line. I take my classroom students to the computer lab and show

them how to use MathXL and the videos. I recommend that anyone who has difficulty with a topic review that material by watching the video and then try some practice problems on MathXL.

■ My on-line students are required to watch the digital video tutors as part of the course. I don't believe that I could teach on-line without the videos. Students need to see and hear someone teaching math. They cannot learn the material by reading my "mini-lectures" or by reading the text. My students have told me that they never would have passed without the videos. I encourage my on-line students to use MathXL because of the tutorial features. I like MathXL because it shows examples similar to the homework problems and gives students the option to use the "guided" solutions

■ I have developed my own resources for Introductory Algebra. They include worksheets, self-paced review materials, and handouts of key concepts. I have typed them to look professional by using the equation editor in Microsoft® Word. An icon for the equation editor can be put on the tool bar to make it very easy to insert fractions, radicals, etc. (Click on "Tools" then "Customize" then "Commands" then "Insert" then scroll down to the "square root icon" that represents "Equation Editor." This icon can be dragged to the tool bar.) I have shown this procedure to at least 12 instructors at my college because they did not know that equation editor exists. It is no longer necessary to hand draw anything on worksheet, quizzes or exams. All materials can look professional.

Roy West, *Robeson Community College*

■ I use TestGen-EQ to generate all of my tests. I believe that retesting in developmental courses is very helpful. I retest on all chapters. TestGen-EQ allows me to be able to do this. After students take the first test (usually multiple choice) we look at the errors they made and try to fix them. Then they are retested on the material to see how much they have improved. This usually encourages the developmental student to relax a little while taking the test. This would be very difficult to do without TestGen-EQ.

■ There are three sources of information that Addison-Wesley provides that are very helpful. The first is MathXL. It provides students who are computer literate (most are) with sources of instruction, guided practice, or just additional problems to work at home. I use MathXL often in class to get students comfortable in using it, and I also use it to generate examples to do in class. The second is the math videos that accompany the text. I have set up two places on campus where students can go and view the videos on any chapter in the textbook. This is helpful for those who missed a class or who are struggling on a particular topic and need to see some more instruction. The third is the Tutor Center, which is a toll-free number that students can call to get help on any example or odd-numbered problem they are working on. Students are normally shy about calling this source because they are talking to someone live on the phone, but some do use it often.

Annette Wiesner,
University of Wisconsin-Parkside

■ I encourage my students to use the videos provided with the text. I suggest them for students who miss class and need to catch-up and also to be used as a quick review before a test. I think these "mini-lectures" are great.

USEFUL OUTSIDE RESOURCES FOR TEACHERS

Texts

Daniel Chazan. *Beyond Formulas in Mathematics and Teaching: Dynamics of the High School Algebra Classroom*, © 2000, Teachers College Press, Columbia University, 9780807739181

C. M. Charles. *Essential Elements of Effective Discipline*, © 2002, Allyn & Bacon. 9780201729481

Randy Davidson & Ellen Levitov. *Overcoming Math Anxiety*, Second Edition, © 2000, Addison-Wesley. 9780321069184

David W. Johnson & Roger T. Johnson. *Meaningful Assessment: A Manageable and Cooperative Process*, © 2002, Allyn & Bacon. 9780205327621

Vernon F. Jones & Louise S. Jones. *Comprehensive Classroom Management: Creating Communities of Support and Solving Problems*, Ninth Edition, © 2010, Allyn & Bacon. 9780205625482

Journal of Developmental Education, National Association for Developmental Education (NADE).

Kane, Michael B., and Ruth Mitchell, eds. *Implementing Performance Assessment: Promises, Problems and Challenges*, © 1996, Lawrence Erlbaum Associates, Inc. 9780805821321

Liping Ma. *Knowing and Teaching Elementary Mathematics*, Second Edition © 2010, Routledge, 9780415873840

Math Spanish Glossary, Second Edition, © 2001, Addison-Wesley. 9780201728965

Mathematics Teacher, National Council of Teachers of Mathematics (NCTM) monthly journal.

W. James Popham. *Classroom Assessment: What Teachers Need to Know*, Sixth Edition, © 2011, Allyn & Bacon. 9780137002337

Thomas A. Romberg, Editor. *Mathematics Assessment and Evaluation: Imperatives for Mathematics Educators*, © 1992, State University of New York Press. 9780791409008

Ruth Stavy & Dina Tirosh. *How Students (Mis-) Understand Science and Mathematics*, © 2000, Teachers College Press, Columbia University. 9780807739587

Suskie, Linda. *Assessing Student Learning: A Common Sense Guide*, Second Edition © 2002, Jossey-Bass. 9780470289648

David F. Treagust, Reinders Duit, & Barry J. Fraser, Editors. *Improving Teaching and Learning in Science and Mathematics*, © 1995, Teachers College Press, Columbia University. 9780807734797

John Webb & Nitsa Movshovitz-Hadar. *One Equals Zero: And Other Mathematical Surprises*, © 1997, Key Curriculum Press. 9781559533096

Norman L. Webb, Editor. *Assessment in the Mathematics Classroom*, © 1993, National Council of Teachers of Mathematics. 9780873533522

Web Links

www.AlgebraHelp.com   Math help using technology

www.Algebra.com   Help with algebra homework on-line

www.amatyc.org   American Mathematics Association of Two Year Colleges

www.coolmath.com   Resources for teachers and students. (some pages may require a subscription)

www.edhelper.com   Lesson plans, teacher resources, etc.

http://www-history.mcs.st-and.ac.uk/history/   The MacTutor History of Mathematics archive

http://horizon.unc.edu/TS/   The Technology Source

www.ictcm.org   International Conference on Technology in Collegiate Mathematics

www.maa.org   Mathematics Association of America

http://mathforum.org/math.topics.html   The Math Forum @ Drexel University

www.mathnstuff.com   Descriptions for some good mathematics manipulatives.

www.mathxl.com

http://www.mcli.dist.maricopa.edu/tl/   Teaching and Learning on the Web

www.merlot.org   Math applications, worksheets, puzzles, etc.

www.micro.magnet.fsu.edu/electromag/java/abacus/   Movable Abacus

www.mymathlab.com

www.nctm.org   The National Council of Teachers of Mathematics

www.PurpleMath.com   Algebra lessons

www.shodor.org/interactivate/activities/ArithmeticFour   Arithmetic Game

www.shodor.org/interactivate/activities/FractionPointer   Number Line Values

www.superkids.com   Including reviews of educational software

www.nade.net   National Association for Developmental Education

www.uoregon.edu/~tep/technology/   University of Oregon Teaching Effectiveness Program

CONVERSION GUIDE

This conversion guide is designed to help you adapt your syllabus for Bittinger *Introductory Algebra*, Tenth Edition to Bittinger *Introductory Algebra*, Eleventh Edition by providing a section-by-section cross reference between the two books. Additional revisions and refinements have been made in addition to the changes specified here.

Sect.	*Introductory Algebra*, Tenth Edition	Sect.	*Introductory Algebra*, Eleventh Edition
R.1	Factoring and LCMs	R.1	Factoring and LCMs
R.2	Fraction Notation	R.2	Fraction Notation
R.3	Decimal Notation	R.3	Decimal Notation
R.4	Percent Notation	R.4	Percent Notation
R.5	Exponential Notation and Order of Operations	R.5	Exponential Notation and Order of Operations
R.6	Geometry	R.6	Geometry
1.1	Introduction to Algebra	1.1	Introduction to Algebra
1.2	The Real Numbers	1.2	The Real Numbers
1.3	Addition of Real Numbers	1.3	Addition of Real Numbers
1.4	Subtraction of Real Numbers	1.4	Subtraction of Real Numbers
1.5	Multiplication of Real Numbers	1.5	Multiplication of Real Numbers
1.6	Division of Real Numbers	1.6	Division of Real Numbers
1.7	Properties of Real Numbers	1.7	Properties of Real Numbers
1.8	Simplifying Expressions; Order of Operations	1.8	Simplifying Expressions; Order of Operations
2.1	Solving Equations: The Addition Principle	2.1	Solving Equations: The Addition Principle
2.2	Solving Equations: The Multiplication Principle	2.2	Solving Equations: The Multiplication Principle
2.3	Using the Principles Together	2.3	Using the Principles Together
2.4	Formulas	2.4	Formulas
2.5	Applications of Percent	2.5	Applications of Percent
2.6	Applications and Problem Solving	2.6	Applications and Problem Solving
2.7	Solving Inequalities	2.7	Solving Inequalities
2.8	Applications and Problem Solving with Inequalities	2.8	Applications and Problem Solving with Inequalities
3.1	Graphs and Applications of Linear Equations	3.1	Graphs and Applications of Linear Equations
3.2	More with Graphing and Intercepts	3.2	More with Graphing and Intercepts
3.3	Slope and Applications	3.3	Slope and Applications
3.4	Equations of Lines	3.4	Equations of Lines
3.5	Graphing Using the Slope and the *y*-Intercept	3.5	Graphing Using the Slope and the *y*-Intercept
3.6	Parallel and Perpendicular Lines	3.6	Parallel and Perpendicular Lines
3.7	Graphing Inequalities in Two Variables	3.7	Graphing Inequalities in two Variables
4.1	Integers as Exponents	4.1	Integers as Exponents

Sect.	*Introductory Algebra*, Tenth Edition	Sect.	*Introductory Algebra*, Eleventh Edition
4.2	Exponents and Scientific Notation	4.2	Exponents and Scientific Notation
4.3	Introduction to Polynomials	4.3	Introduction to Polynomials
4.4	Addition and Subtraction of Polynomials	4.4	Addition and Subtraction of Polynomials
4.5	Multiplication of Polynomials	4.5	Multiplication of Polynomials
4.6	Special Products	4.6	Special Products
4.7	Operations with Polynomials in Several Variables	4.7	Operations with Polynomials in Several Variables
4.8	Division of Polynomials	4.8	Division of Polynomials
5.1	Introduction to Factoring	5.1	Introduction to Factoring
5.2	Factoring Trinomials of the Type $x^2 + bx + c$	5.2	Factoring Trinomials of the Type $x^2 + bx + c$
5.3	Factoring $ax^2 + bx + c, a \neq 1$: The FOIL Method	5.3	Factoring $ax^2 + bx + c, a \neq 1$: The FOIL Method
5.4	Factoring $ax^2 + bx + c, a \neq 1$: The ac-Method	5.4	Factoring $ax^2 + bx + c, a \neq 1$: The ac-Method
5.5	Factoring Trinomial Squares and Differences of Squares	5.5	Factoring Trinomial Squares and Differences of Squares
5.6	Factoring: A General Strategy	5.6	Factoring: A General Strategy
5.7	Solving Quadratic Equations by Factoring	5.7	Solving Quadratic Equations by Factoring
5.8	Applications of Quadratic Equations	5.8	Applications of Quadratic Equations
6.1	Multiplying and Simplifying Rational Expressions	6.1	Multiplying and Simplifying Rational Expressions
6.2	Division and Reciprocals	6.2	Division and Reciprocals
6.3	Least Common Multiples and Denominators	6.3	Least Common Multiples and Denominators
6.4	Adding Rational Expressions	6.4	Adding Rational Expressions
6.5	Subtracting Rational Expressions	6.5	Subtracting Rational Expressions
6.6	Solving Rational Equations	6.6	Solving Rational Equations
6.7	Applications Using Rational Equations and Proportions	6.7	Applications Using Rational Equations and Proportions
6.8	Complex Rational Expressions	6.8	Complex Rational Expressions
6.9	Direct and Inverse Variation	6.9	Direct Variation and Inverse Variation
7.1	Systems of Equations in Two Variables	7.1	Systems of Equations in Two Variables
7.2	The Substitution Method	7.2	The Substitution Method
7.3	The Elimination Method	7.3	The Elimination Method
7.4	Applications and Problem Solving	7.4	Applications and Problem Solving
7.5	Applications with Motion	7.5	Applications with Motion
8.1	Introduction to Radical Expressions	8.1	Introduction to Radical Expressions
8.2	Multiplying and Simplifying with Radical Expressions	8.2	Multiplying and Simplifying with Radical Expressions
8.3	Quotients Involving Radical Expressions	8.3	Quotients Involving Radical Expressions
8.4	Addition, Subtraction, and More Multiplication	8.4	Addition, Subtraction, and More Multiplication
8.5	Radical Equations	8.5	Radical Equations
8.6	Applications with Right Triangles	8.6	Applications with Right Triangles
9.1	Introduction to Quadratic Equations	9.1	Introduction to Quadratic Equations
9.2	Solving Quadratic Equations by Completing the Square	9.2	Solving Quadratic Equations by Completing the Square
9.3	The Quadratic Formula	9.3	The Quadratic Formula

Sect.	*Introductory Algebra*, Tenth Edition	Sect.	*Introductory Algebra*, Eleventh Edition
9.4	Formulas	9.4	Formulas
9.5	Applications and Problem Solving	9.5	Applications and Problem Solving
9.6	Graphs of Quadratic Equations	9.6	Graphs of Quadratic Equations
9.7	Functions	9.7	Functions
A	Factoring Sums or Differences of Cubes	A	Factoring Sums of Differences of Cubes
B	Finding Equations of Lines: Point-Slope Equation	B	Finding Equations of Lines: Point-Slope Equation
C	Higher Roots	C	Higher Roots
D	Sets	D	Sets
E	Mean, Median, and Mode	E	Mean, Median, and Mode

VIDEO AND EXERCISE INDEX

Section	Chapter & Section Titles	Examples from Text Covered	Exercises from Text Covered
Ch R	**Prealgebra Review**		
R.1	Factoring and LCMs	4	3, 17, 29
R.2	Fraction Notation	2, 6, 7, 17, 18	7, 17, 39, 45
R.3	Decimal Notation	5, 7, 12, 13	5, 11, 21, 51, 73
R.4	Percent Notation	None	23, 29
R.5	Exponential Notation and Order of Operations	2	31, 61
R.6	Geometry	4, 11	3, 41, 43, 51
Ch 1	**Introduction to Real Numbers and Algebraic Expressions**		
1.1	Introduction to Algebra	1, 2, 8, 9, 12	15, 43
1.2	The Real Numbers	9, 25, 26, 27, 28, 29, 30	3, 9, 11, 15, 31, 39, 41, 47, 57
1.3	Addition of Real Numbers	1, 2, 3, 4, 13, 19, 24	9, 21, 23, 31, 41, 55, 57, 69
1.4	Subtraction of Real Numbers	1, 11, 12, 13	7, 55, 73
1.5	Multiplication of Real Numbers	1, 6, 7, 17	11, 33, 35, 37, 41
1.6	Division of Real Numbers	24	3, 13, 25, 29, 35, 51, 65
1.7	Properties of Real Numbers	1, 2, 11, 14, 27, 34, 37	1, 9, 17, 21, 53, 81, 94, 97
1.8	Simplifying Expressions; Order of Operations	4, 6	5, 25, 39, 45, 61, 81
Ch 2	**Solving Equations and Inequalities**		
2.1	Solving Equations: The Addition Principle	5, 9	33
2.2	Solving Equations: The Multiplication Principle	3	3, 29
2.3	Using the Principles Together	2, 6	1, 29, 47, 63, 65, 83
2.4	Formulas	1	7, 21, 33, 41, 51
2.5	Applications of Percent	3	5, 19, 21, 43, 47
2.6	Applications and Problem Solving	None	15
2.7	Solving Inequalities	1, 2, 3, 4	7, 9, 11, 17, 23, 37, 45, 61, 71
2.8	Applications and Problem Solving with Inequalities	None	11, 15, 17, 19, 27
Ch 3	**Graphs of Linear Equations**		
3.1	Graphs and Applications of Linear Equations	2	21, 29, 43, 59
3.2	More with Graphing and Intercepts	None	13, 37, 43, 49
3.3	Slope and Applications	4	9, 31, 43, 55
3.4	Equations of Lines	None	7, 13, 17, 19, 31, 33
3.5	Graphing Using the Slope and the y-intercept	None	1, 5, 13, 25
3.6	Parallel and Perpendicular Lines	None	1, 7, 11, 13, 19, 23, 27
3.7	Graphing Inequalities in Two Variables	3, 6	3, 19, 25

Section	Chapter & Section Titles	Examples from Text Covered	Exercises from Text Covered
Ch 4	**Polynomials: Operations**		
4.1	Integers as Exponents	4, 9, 16	17, 23, 35, 49, 83, 101
4.2	Exponents and Scientific Notation	2, 11, 20	5, 53, 57, 67, 89
4.3	Introduction to Polynomials	9, 20	9, 35, 85, 93, 95, 97, 99
4.4	Addition and Subtraction of Polynomials	10, 11, 12	7, 17, 31, 43, 53
4.5	Multiplication of Polynomials	2, 4, 7, 9	5, 41, 65, 73
4.6	Special Products	1, 5, 9, 14, 19, 27, 28	5, 33, 51, 63, 81, 91
4.7	Operations with Polynomials in Several Variables	3, 6, 12	3, 9, 29, 37, 61, 75, 77
4.8	Division of Polynomials	2, 4, 9	17, 29
Ch 5	**Polynomials: Factoring**		
5.1	Introduction to Factoring	1, 4	7, 15, 21, 27, 47
5.2	Factoring Trinomials of the Type $x^2 + bx + c$	2, 3	1, 23, 31
5.3	Factoring $ax^2 + bx + c, a \neq 1$; The FOIL Method	1	31
5.4	Factoring $ax^2 + bx + c, a \neq 1$; The *ac*-Method	1	1, 7, 19, 69
5.5	Factoring Trinomial Squares and Differences of Squares	11, 12	1, 3, 5, 9, 21, 23, 43, 45, 55 65, 67, 81
5.6	Factoring: A General Strategy	1, 4, 5, 9	9, 13, 39, 51, 71
5.7	Solving Quadratic Equations by Factoring	1, 5	13, 17, 37
5.8	Applications of Quadratic Equations	4	4, 7
Ch 6	**Rational Expressions and Equations**		
6.1	Multiplying and Simplifying Rational Expressions	3, 11	9, 25, 29, 47
6.2	Division and Reciprocals	1, 2	3, 5, 13, 17, 33
6.3	Least Common Multiples and Denominators	1, 6	13, 19, 37
6.4	Adding Rational Expressions	1, 6, 11	4, 9, 59
6.5	Subtracting Rational Expressions	2	13, 29, 35, 37, 51
6.6	Solving Rational Equations	1, 4	11, 27, 39
6.7	Applications Using Rational Equations and Proportions	None	17, 49
6.8	Complex Rational Expressions	1, 4	7, 9, 13, 15
6.9	Direct and Inverse Variation	1, 4	7, 17, 31
Ch 7	**Systems of Equations**		
7.1	Systems of Equations in Two Variables	None	13, 11, 17, 23
7.2	The Substitution Method	None	1, 19, 21, 27
7.3	The Elimination Method	6	9, 19
7.4	Applications and Problem Solving	3, 5	none
7.5	Applications with Motion	1	3, 9

Section	Chapter & Section Titles	Examples from Text Covered	Exercises from Text Covered
Ch 8	**Radical Expressions and Equations**		
8.1	Introduction to Radical Expressions	2, 3, 5, 7, 11, 16	7, 27, 43, 45, 47, 65
8.2	Multiplying and Simplifying with Radical Expressions	1, 4, 10	7, 25, 51, 65, 85
8.3	Quotients Involving Radical Expressions	2	1, 15, 27, 33, 53
8.4	Addition, Subtraction, and More Multiplication	2, 6, 10	1, 23, 49, 57, 59
8.5	Radical Equations	1, 6	13, 21, 39
8.6	Applications with Right Triangles	3	3, 17
Ch 9	**Quadratic Equations**		
9.1	Introduction to Quadratic Equations	3, 4, 7, 9	3, 19, 57
9.2	Solving Quadratic Equations by Completing the Square	None	9, 23, 47, 55
9.3	The Quadratic Formula	1	21
9.4	Formulas	1, 3, 6	11, 25, 43
9.5	Applications and Problem Solving	2	2
9.6	Graphs of Quadratic Equations	1	11, 17, 33
9.7	Functions	1, 7, 8	15a, 17d, 19c, 21e, 35, 41

Activity R.5   Use the order of operations to modify an expression.

Focus	Order of operations
Time	10–15 minutes
Group size	2
Background	Understanding the rules for order of operations is essential to your study of algebra. This activity provides you with a different perspective on using the rules, and should help you learn the order of operations.

1. Write down the rules for order of operations in the space below. Refer to Section R.5 in your textbook, if needed.

2. The object of this activity is to insert grouping and/or operation symbols within a display of numbers in order to obtain a predetermined result. The symbols allowed are: $(\ )$, $+$, $-$, $\cdot$, and $\div$. For example, let's start with the display shown below.

$$1 \qquad 2 \qquad 3 \qquad 4 \qquad 5$$

When you insert the symbols as follows,

$$(1+2) \div 3 + 4 \cdot 5,$$

the result will be 21. Check that this is correct by simplifying the expression.

On the other hand, if you insert symbols in a different way, as shown below,

$$1 + (2+3) \cdot 4 - 5,$$

the result is 16. Check this by simplifying the expression.

3. Now, prepare an exercise for your partner to solve. Select five single-digit numbers (from 1 to 9) for display. Then, privately, insert grouping symbols and/or operations

---

within your display, and calculate the result. Write the result and the display of numbers on a blank sheet of paper, and exchange papers with your partner.

On the paper you receive, insert symbols so as to make the display equal the number given. When you are done, exchange papers again. Check your partner's solution with yours. Discuss any differences you find.

4. If you have time, prepare another exercise for your partner to solve.

Conclusion	The process of inserting symbols into a display of numbers should give you a good understanding of the rules for order of operations. It is also fun to manipulate symbols to achieve a predetermined goal.

Activity 1.3   Add integers using a variety of methods.

Focus	Addition of integers
Time	20–25 minutes
Group size	4
Materials	Ruler
Background	A variety of methods is used to help students gain an understanding of addition of integers. Section 1.3 of your textbook shows addition on a number line and addition using rules. Another method that is quite effective is addition using tiles. This activity will give you practice with all three methods.
Instructor notes	Copy the page of tiles on card stock, and cut out the tiles. Each group will need one set of tiles. You can also purchase sets of color tiles from ETA/Cuisenaire. If you choose to use color tiles, you will need to modify the instructions for step 3.

1. The three methods we will be working with are listed below.

    Number Line Method

    Color Tile Method

    Rule Method

    The following problems will be used to practice each of these methods.

    $$5 + (-7) \ = \ \underline{\hspace{2cm}}$$
    $$-3 + (-9) \ = \ \underline{\hspace{2cm}}$$
    $$-8 + 3 \ = \ \underline{\hspace{2cm}}$$

2. Number Line Method

    Draw a number line on a piece of ruled notebook paper. Turn the paper sideways and draw the line across the middle of the page. Mark the number 0 in the middle of the line, then mark the positive and negative integers. Use the ruled lines on the page to help space out the integers.

    Read the beginning of Section 1.3 of your textbook for the guidelines on using the number line. Remember that you move to the right if a number is positive, and to the left if the number is negative. If you like, show this on your number line by writing a "+" above the rightmost end of the line, and a "–" above the leftmost end.

To add 5 + (–7), start at 0 and move 5 units right since 5 is positive, then move _____ units to the left. You should end up at the point _____, so the answer is _____. Practice with the other two examples. If your group needs more practice, create additional problems, or work some problems from your textbook.

3. Tile Method

With this method, positive integers are represented by tiles with a "+" sign, while negative integer tiles have a "–" sign. When combining tiles, a positive tile and a negative tile add to 0, thus creating a "zero pair", which is removed.

Practice adding integers using this model. The first example is 5 + (–7). Represent 5 with five positive tiles and –7 with seven negative tiles. Put both groups together, and remove all zero pairs, and count the tiles remaining. In this case, there are _____ tiles, all _____, so the answer is _____.

Continue practicing addition with this tile model, until everyone in the group is comfortable with the process.

4. Rule Method

Refer to Section 1.3 of your textbook for the different rules for adding integers. For reference, write a brief description of each rule in the table below. Be sure to use complete sentences.

Positive + Positive	
Negative + Negative	
Positive + Negative OR Negative + Positive	

Now, do the examples using these rules. As before, practice adding integers until each group member is proficient with the method.

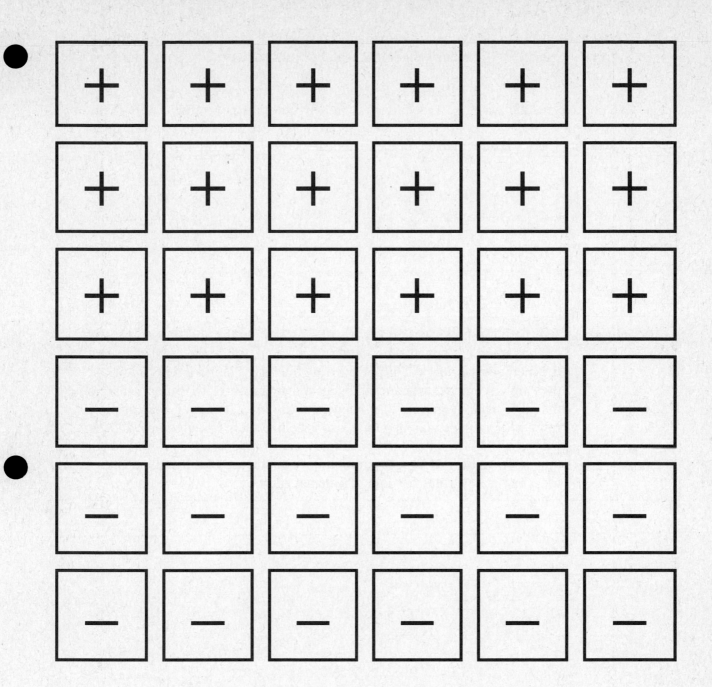

5. For the second part of this activity, each group member chooses one of the three addition methods. The fourth group member takes the role of the question generator.

To begin, the question generator creates an integer addition problem. The problem can have up to five numbers, and should contain a mix of positive and negative integers. Keep the values between –15 and + 15, to accommodate the model restraints.

Write the problem down on a piece of paper so the other group members can clearly see the numbers. Then read out the problem slowly while the other group members work the problem using their chosen method. When all group members are finished, compare answers. If the answers do not match, check each other's work, and redo the problem as needed.

Continue in this way two more times, with the question generator creating 2 more problems. Then, rotate roles so that each group member takes a turn as the question generator, and works with each of the methods.

| Conclusion | This activity shows you three ways of representing the addition of integers. Each method has advantages and disadvantages. While the number line and tile methods are very useful for showing the logic behind integer addition, they are not practical for adding integers that are large. The rule method, on the other hand, works well for integers of any size. However, memorizing rules without understanding the reasons behind them is dangerous, and can lead to difficulties later on in your study of algebra. Ideally, you would gain the understanding of integer addition through the use of the number line or tiles, but use the rules for doing the actual addition. |

Activity 1.4   Subtract integers using tiles.

Focus	Subtraction of integers
Time	15–20 minutes
Group size	2
Background	We subtract integers by adding the opposite of the number being subtracted, as described in Section 1.4 of your textbook. On a more basic level, subtraction corresponds to "take away". In this activity, "take away" will be used to subtract integers when working with tiles.
Instructor notes	Copy the next page on card stock, and cut out the tiles. Each group will need two pages worth of tiles. You can also purchase sets of color tiles from Cuisenaire Dale Seymour Publications. If you choose to use color tiles, you will need to modify the instructions for step 1.

1. Note: If your group has done Activity 1.3, and is proficient with using positive and negative tiles to add integers, skip ahead to step 2.

   With the tile model, positive integers are represented by tiles with a "+" sign, while negative integer tiles have a "−" sign. When combining tiles, a positive tile and a negative tile add to 0, thus creating a "zero pair", and are removed.

2. For this activity, one group member holds all the positive tiles, while the other keeps the negative tiles. Practice combining positive and negative tiles. Each group member places several of his or her tiles on the table. It does not matter how many of each you select. Together, remove all zero pairs, and count the remaining tiles left on the table. There should be only one kind of tile. Practice combining tiles until both of you are proficient with this process.

3. Now, let's see how subtraction is done using the tiles. Consider the problem

$$9 - 5 = \text{_____}$$

   Represent 9 with nine positive tiles. Since subtraction means "take away", you will remove five positive tiles from the group. The tiles that are left represent the answer to the problem. Next, look at the problem

$$-7 - (-2) = \text{_____}$$

   Start with seven negative tiles and take away two negative tiles. The answer is represented by the remaining tiles.

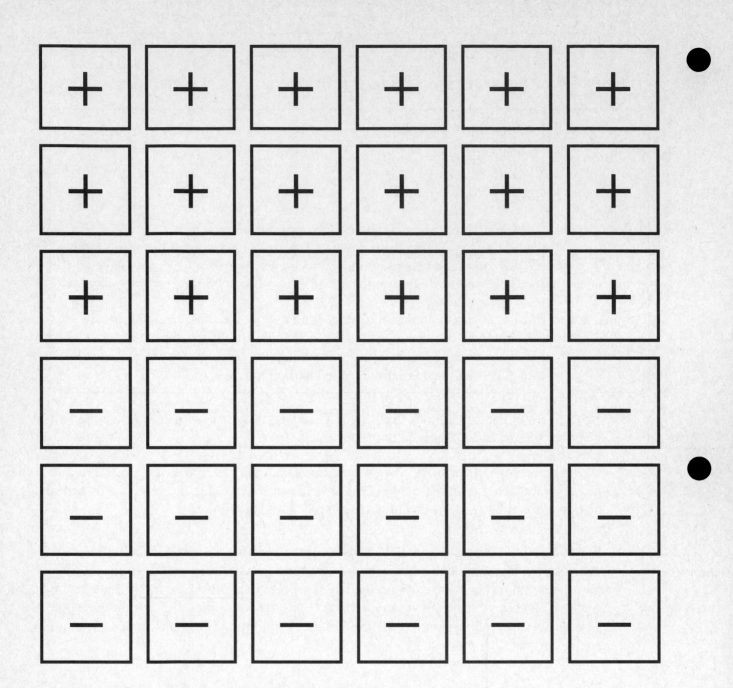

Introductory Algebra   Collaborative Learning Activities

Practice this process on the following problems.

$$7 - 4 = \underline{\qquad}$$
$$-9 - (-5) = \underline{\qquad}$$
$$-6 - (-4) = \underline{\qquad}$$

4. Once you are proficient with the problems in the previous step, you can move on to more complex situations. Consider the problem

$$3 - 8 = \underline{\qquad}$$

As before, start with three positive tiles, and try to take away eight positive tiles. This is not possible, since there are not enough positive tiles to remove. To resolve this difficulty, add more positive tiles to the group until there are enough to take away. You will need to add an equal number of negative tiles so that the problem is not altered. Remember that adding zero pairs is equivalent to adding the number 0. Remove eight positive tiles, and count the remaining tiles in the group to get your answer.

Use the color tile method to do the following subtraction problems.

$$2 - 9 = \underline{\qquad}$$
$$1 - 7 = \underline{\qquad}$$
$$-3 - (-8) = \underline{\qquad}$$
$$2 - (-4) \ = \underline{\qquad}$$
$$-6 - (-6) = \underline{\qquad}$$
$$-1 - 7 \ = \underline{\qquad}$$
$$3 - 5 = \underline{\qquad}$$
$$3 - (-5) = \underline{\qquad}$$
$$-3 - (-5) = \underline{\qquad}$$
$$-3 - 5 = \underline{\qquad}$$

Conclusion	The color tile method gives you a visual, hands-on model for integer subtraction. Use this model to help you understand why the rules for subtraction work, and to develop greater proficiency in subtracting integers.

Activity 1.7   Use the commutative and associative laws to add a series of numbers.

Focus	Commutative and associative laws
Time	15–20 minutes
Group size	2-3
Background	Legend has it that while still in grade school, the mathematician Carl Freidrich Gauss (1777–1855) was able to add the numbers from 1 to 100 mentally. Gauss did not add them from left to right; instead, he paired the numbers 1 and 99, 2 and 98, 3 and 97, and so on, such that each pair added to 100. In this activity, you will use a method similar to Gauss's method to add a series of numbers.

1. Follow the steps given below to simplify the expression. You will be pairing numbers as Gauss did (see background).

$$1 + 2 + 3 + 4 + 5 + 6 + 7 + 8 + 9 + 10$$

Which numbers will you pair up?

What will each pair of numbers add to?

How many pairs will there be? Is there any number left over?

Calculate the sum using the pairs.

Check your answer by adding the numbers from left to right. Use a calculator if you wish.

2. Explain how the associative and commutative laws of addition were used in your calculations above.

3. Next, use Gauss's method to find the sum of the first 100 natural numbers:

$$1 + 2 + 3 + \ldots + 48 + 49 + 50 + 51 + 52 + \ldots + 97 + 98 + 99 + 100$$

Sum of each pair   _____

Number of pairs   _____

Leftover number   _____

Total sum   _____

Compare your group's answers with those of another group.

4. Using a method similar to Gauss', find the sum of the first 200 natural numbers.

Sum of each pair   _____

Number of pairs   _____

Leftover number   _____

Total sum   _____

Conclusion	As you saw in this activity, the properties of real numbers can help you quickly add long sums of numbers. Use this method whenever you need to add mentally. You might even impress your friends with your mathematical prowess!

Activity 1.8   Use the order of operations as a group to simplify expressions.

Focus	Order of operations
Time	20–30 minutes
Group size	3
Background	Simplifying expressions using the rules for order of operations can be quite confusing for complicated expressions. Learning to simplify expressions as a group will help clarify the process.

Rules for Order of Operations

	Do all calculations within parentheses before operations outside.
E	Evaluate all exponential expressions.
MD	Do all multiplications and divisions in order from left to right.
AS	Do all additions and subtractions in order from left to right.

1. Before you begin simplifying expressions, study the rules for order of operations above. Assign each group member to one of the steps listed. Write the name of the group member next to his or her assigned task in the table above. Note that the first step (calculations within parentheses) is not assigned. All group members will do this step together.

2. Now you are ready to simplify expressions as a group. Analyze the expression together and decide on the first step. If there are parentheses, decide whether the expression inside the parentheses needs to be simplified. Following the order of operations, **E** will perform his or her task before **MD,** and **MD** will perform his or her task before **AS.**

   Practice with the example on the next page. (This is Example 22, Section 1.8 in your textbook.) The first step has been done for you: Multiply inside the parentheses. **MD** will do this step, writing **"MD"** in the left box, and writing the new expression below the original expression.

   Continue simplifying the expression by passing the problem to the appropriate group member for the next step. When you are done, compare your steps to those in Example 22, Section 1.8 in your textbook. If there are any discrepancies, discuss them within your group. Compare your result with the other groups. Are they the same? Discuss any differences with the other groups.

Example 22, Section 1.8

	$-2^4 + 51 \cdot 4 - (37 + 23 \cdot 2)$
MD	$-2^4 + 51 \cdot 4 - (37 + 46)$

3. Once you understand the process, choose an expression from exercises 41 to 82 in Exercise Set 1.8 in your textbook to simplify as a group. Use the table on the next page to organize your work. Make as many copies as you need. Alternatively, you can draw the table on a blank sheet of paper.

Do as many problems as you can in the time allotted. Make sure you choose at least one of the more complicated expressions from the last part of the exercise set.

Conclusion	This activity should help you gain a better understanding of the rules for order of operations. You can also use this group method to simplify algebraic expressions such as $3y - 2(4y - 5)$.

Original expression _____

Introductory Algebra   Collaborative Learning Activities

Activity 2.1   Pair It Up!

Focus	Solving Equations : The Addition Principle
Time	15–20 minutes
Group size	2–4
Material	Card stock rectangles
Background	This activity will give you practice with solving equations using the Addition Principle. You will need to solve these equations mentally as quickly as you can.

1. Put equations on one side of 10 cards with answers to these equations on 10 other cards.

2. Number the cards randomly 1-20.

3. Mix the cards and put them down on the table number-side up.

4. Each team member chooses 2 cards one at a time. Return cards if the equation and its answer are not chosen (similar to the game Concentration).

5. Pair the equation with its answer.

6. Play continues until all pairs are chosen.

7. The winner has the most pairs.

Conclusion	Exercise Set 2.1 in your textbook includes a variety of equations. Solve these equations using the addition principle.

$x+2=11$	$x+5=-8$	$t-3=19$	$x+\dfrac{1}{2}=-\dfrac{3}{2}$	$x-7=-21$
$-8+y=17$	$8+y=12$	$x+\dfrac{1}{2}=7$	$m+18=-13$	$-7+y=13$

9	-13	22	-2	-14
25	4	$6\frac{1}{2}$	-31	20

Activity 2.2   Spin It Fast!

Focus	Solving Equations: The Multiplication Principle
Time	15–30 minutes
Group size	2–4
Materials	Spinner with numbers 1-10, card stock rectangles with equations on one side and numbers 1-10 on the other side.
Background	This activity will give you practice with solving equations using the multiplication principle. You will need to solve these equations mentally as quickly as you can.

1. Make a spinner with 10 numbers and 10 card stock rectangles with equations on one side and numbered 1–10 on the other side. Put the rectangles face-down on the table.

2. Spin and solve the equation with the same number as the number spun. Mark an X over the number on the spinner, so it is "out of commission." If you stop on an "out of commission" number, you lose your turn. The spins rotate through all the players, and the instructor chooses the player who starts first.

3. Each player writes down the number of equations s/he has solved correctly.

4. The player who solves the most equations correctly wins the round.

Conclusion	Exercise Set 2.2 in your textbook includes a variety of equations that can be solved using the multiplication principle.

1	2	3	4	5
6	7	8	9	10

$6x = 90$	$\dfrac{-t}{3} = 7$
$-6x = 108$	$\dfrac{1}{8} = \dfrac{-y}{5}$
$63 = 9x$	$\dfrac{m}{-3} = 10$
$-15x = 105$	$\dfrac{4}{5}x = 16$
$\dfrac{3}{4}x = 27$	$-21x = -126$

Introductory Algebra   Collaborative Learning Activities

Problems	Answers
1) $6x = 90$	$x = 15$
2) $-6x = 108$	$x = -18$
3) $63 = 9x$	$x = 7$
4) $-15x = 105$	$x = -7$
5) $\frac{3}{4}x = 27$	$x = 36$
6) $\frac{-t}{3} = 7$	$t = -21$
7) $\frac{1}{8} = \frac{-y}{5}$	$-\frac{5}{8} = y$
8) $\frac{m}{-3} = 10$	$m = -30$
9) $\frac{4}{5}x = 16$	$x = 20$
10) $-21x = -126$	$x = 6$

Activity 2.3   Solve linear equations as a group.

Focus	Solving linear equations
Time	10–20 minutes
Group size	3
Background	This activity will give you practice with solving equations as a group. There is usually more than one correct sequence of steps for solving an equation. Thus, it is important to be able to follow someone else's steps even if his or her approach is not like yours.

1. Each group member should select a different one of the following equations.

$$2\left[4-2(3-x)\right]-1=4\left[2(4x-3)+7\right]-25$$

$$\frac{5}{3}+\frac{2}{3}x=\frac{25}{12}+\frac{5}{4}x+\frac{3}{4}$$

$$0.8-4(x-1)=0.2+3(4-x)$$

Write the equation on a blank sheet of paper, and perform a first step of the solution.

2. When you are done, pass your paper to the group member on your left. Look at the paper you receive and check the work shown. If you spot an error, discuss it with the group member who did the step. He or she should then correct the error.

3. Perform a second step of the solution for the equation you received. Then pass the paper to the group member on your left.

4. Check the work on the problem you receive. Discuss and correct any errors as before, then do the next step. Continue passing the problems until all equations have been solved.

5. As a group, look at the solutions to all three equations. When you are satisfied with the answers, compare them with the other groups in the class.

Conclusion	Solving equations as a group gives you a better understanding of the solution process. You can also use this technique to solve linear inequalities (see Activity 2.7) or to simplify algebraic expressions in other chapters.

Activity 2.5   Calculate the sale price and original price of discounted items.

Focus	Applications with percents
Time	10–15 minutes
Group size	4
Background	Often a store will reduce the price of an item by a fixed percentage and then return to the original price once the sale is over. This activity will give you practice in calculating the sale price of several items, and help you develop a formula for restoring the original price.

1. Think of an item you would like to purchase, like a jacket or portable stereo, and set a reasonable price for the item. Write the information in the table on the next page, and pass the paper to the group member on your left.

2. Now, suppose the purchased item is on sale. Choose a reasonable discount percent for the item, and write this information in the table. Pass the paper to the group member on your left again.

3. Calculate the discount amount and the sale price of the item you receive. Write your answers in the table, and pass the paper to the group member on your left.

4. Find a multiplier that can be used to convert the discounted price back to the original price. Write this result in the table, and pass the paper again to your left.

5. Check the calculations for the item you receive; if you spot an error, discuss it with the group member who did the step. He or she should then correct the error.

6. When all calculations are correct, examine the tables together as a group, and compare the multipliers for each item. Do the multipliers depend on the price of the item? By what percentage is the discounted price increased when returning to the original price? Use complete sentences in your answer.

7. Develop a formula that can be used to find a multiplier that will restore an r% discounted price to its original price. Check that this formula will duplicate the results for each item.

Item name	
Original price	
Discount percent	
Discount amount	
Sale price	
Multiplier	

Conclusion	Exercise Set 2.5 in your textbook includes a variety of percent problems. Do some of these problems in order to become familiar with the various uses of percent.

Activity 2.7   Solve linear inequalities as a group.

Focus	Solving linear inequalities
Time	10–20 minutes
Group size	3
Background	This activity will give you practice with solving inequalities as a group. There is usually more than one correct sequence of steps for solving an inequality. Thus, it is important to be able to follow someone else's steps even if his or her approach is not like yours.

1. Each group member should select a different one from the following inequalities.

    $$6[4-2(6\ +\ 3x)] > 5[3(7-x)-4(8+2x)]-20$$

    $$1.7x+8-1.62x < 0.4x-0.32+8$$

    $$\frac{7}{12}-\frac{8}{3}x-\frac{5}{8} < \frac{3}{8}$$

    Write the inequality on a blank sheet of paper, and perform a first step of the solution.

2. When you are done, pass your paper to the group member on your left. Look at the paper you receive and check the work shown. If you spot an error, discuss it with the group member who did the step. He or she should then correct the error.

3. Perform a second step of the solution for the inequality you received. Then pass the paper to the group member on your left.

4. Check the work on the problem you receive. Discuss and correct any errors as before, then do the next step. Continue passing the problems until all inequalities have been solved.

5. As a group, look at the solutions to all three inequalities. When you are satisfied with the answers, compare them with the other groups in the class.

Conclusion	Solving inequalities as a group gives you a better understanding of the solution process. You can also use this technique to solve equations (see Activity 2.3) or to simplify expressions in other chapters.

Activity 3.1   Practice finding and plotting ordered pairs by playing a variation of the game Battleship®.

Focus	Plotting ordered pairs
Time	15–25 minutes
Group size	4
Background	In the game Battleship®, each player places miniature ships on a grid that only the player can see. An opponent guesses coordinates that might "hit" one of the "hidden" ships. This activity is similar to the game and gives you practice with finding and plotting points on a coordinate plane.

1. One group member begins by secretly choosing an ordered pair, with x- and y-coordinates between -10 and 10. Record the coordinates of the secret point on a slip of paper and keep it hidden from the other group members. This point will be your "battleship".

2. The other group members in turn try to locate (and sink) the hidden ship. You are only allowed to ask mathematical questions which can be answered with a "yes" or "no". Some examples are given below. Be creative, and refer to Section 3.1 of your textbook for assistance in phrasing your questions.

    Is the first coordinate less than 7?

    Is the ship located on an axis?

    Is the second coordinate negative?

3. After answering each question, the group member who selected the point should use the graph on the next page to shade those points no longer under consideration. The other group members can refer to this graph to help decide their next question.

4. If the hidden battleship has not been sunk after 3 rounds of questions, the ship has "survived" the battle. The group member who owns this ship should reveal its location to the others in the group.

5. Now, switch roles, with another group member selecting a secret location. Continue as before, with the other 3 group members asking questions in an attempt to sink the ship.

6. The game is over when all 4 group members have had a chance to select a battleship location.

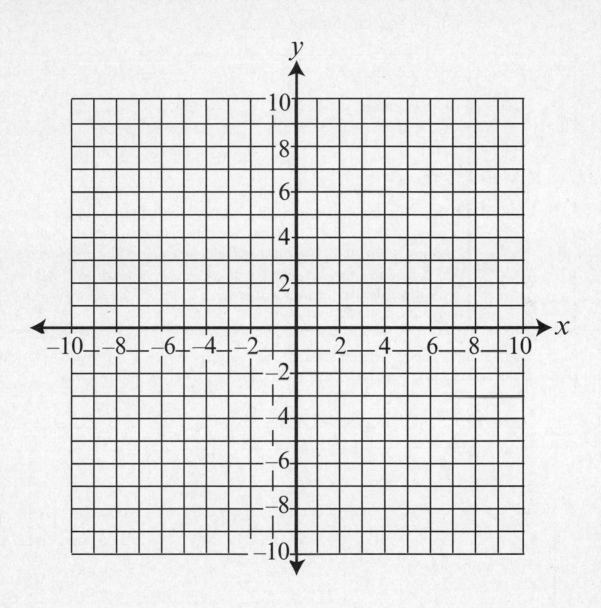

| Conclusion | Plotting ordered pairs is an important skill in your study of algebra. This activity should help you be more proficient at locating and plotting points on a coordinate plane. |

Activity 3.3   Verify that *m* and *b* represent the slope and *y*-intercept of the line $y = mx + b$.

Focus	Slope and *y*-intercept
Time	10–15 minutes
Group size	4
Materials	Graph paper
Background	When a linear equation in *x* and *y* is solved for *y*, the resulting equation is $y = mx + b$. In Section 3.1 of your textbook, you saw that the graph of the equation $y = mx + b$ passes through the *y*-intercept (0, *b*). In Section 3.3, you learned that the coefficient of the *x*-term, *m*, is the slope of the line. We will verify that the values of *m* and *b* do indeed represent the slope and *y*-intercept of a line.

1. Each group member will graph one of the equations below. Write your name next to the equation you choose and identify the values of *m* and *b* in your equation.

Group member	Equation	*m*	*b*
	$y = \dfrac{3}{4}x - 5$		
	$y = \dfrac{3}{4}x + 2$		
	$y = -\dfrac{2}{3}x - 5$		
	$y = -\dfrac{2}{3}x + 2$		

2. Graph the line on graph paper, using any of the methods studied in Chapter 3. Label the scale on each axis, but do not write the equation of the line on the graph. Make sure your graphs are neat and accurate.

3. Exchange graphs with another group member. For the line you are given, find the slope of the graph by measuring the rise and run. Also identify the y-intercept of the line. Write these values next to the graph.

4. Compare your values of m and b with the values written in the table from step 1. Are they identical?

5. Share your findings with the rest of the group. What conclusion can you draw from your observation of the values of m and b? Write your conclusions below.

In the equation $y = mx + b$,

The value of m represents the _____ of the line.

The value of b represents the _____ of the line.

Conclusion	As expected, the values of m and b represent the slope and y-intercept, respectively, of the line $y = mx + b$. An extension of these facts would enable you to graph the line $y = mx + b$ by using the y-intercept $(0, b)$ and the slope m to plot points for the line. This will be done in Section 3.5.

Activity 3.7   Practice graphing linear inequalities by playing a variation of the game Battleship®.

Focus	Linear inequalities
Time	15–25 minutes
Group size	4
Materials	Graph paper
Background	In the game Battleship®, each player places miniature ships on a grid that only the player can see. An opponent guesses at coordinates that might "hit" one of the "hidden" ships. This activity is similar to the game, but the opponents must ask questions that are phrased as linear inequalities.

Note: This activity is similar to the activity done in Section 3.1. However, instead of asking questions based on coordinate points, you will ask questions using linear inequalities.

1. One group member begins by secretly choosing an ordered pair. Record the coordinates of the secret point on a slip of paper and keep it hidden from the other group members. This point will be your "battleship".

2. The other group members in turn must try to locate (and sink) the hidden ship. You are only allowed to ask mathematical questions of the following two types, both of which can be answered with a "yes" or "no".

    Are the point's coordinates a solution of $y > x$?

    Are the coordinates of the hidden point (–3, 7)?

Refer to Section 3.7 of your textbook for assistance in phrasing your questions.

3. After answering each question, the group member who selected the point should use the graph on the next page to shade those points no longer under consideration. The other group members can refer to this graph to help decide their next question.

4. If the hidden battleship has not been sunk after 3 rounds of questions, the ship has "survived" the battle. The group member who owns this ship should reveal its location to the others in the group.

5. Now, switch roles, with another group member selecting a secret location. Continue as before, with the other 3 group members asking questions in an attempt to sink the ship.

6. The game is over when all 4 group members have had a chance to select a battleship location.

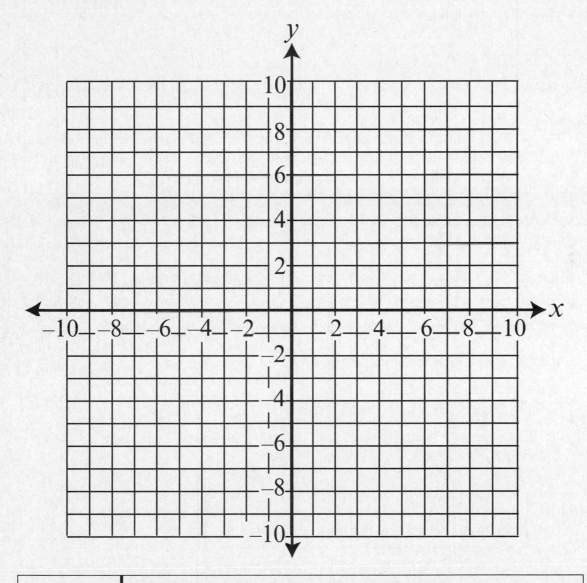

| Conclusion | Graphing linear inequalities is an important skill in your study of algebra. This activity should give you a better understanding of the topic. |

Activity 4.1   Ring It!

Focus	Integers as Exponents
Time	15–30 minutes
Group size	2–4
Materials	24-ounce bottles (20) and 1 ring hoop (plastic), 20 problems with answers
Background	This activity will give you practice in evaluating exponential expressions and algebraic expressions containing exponents, using the Product Rule to multiply exponential expressions with like bases, and using the Quotient Rule to divide exponential expressions with like bases.

1. Each member of the team tosses 1 ring at the bottles. Each person has 3 chances to ring the bottle.

2. If the toss hits the target, the student does the next problem. (Variation: Write the problems on card stock and number them 1 – 20. The student chooses a number and does that problem.)

3. If the toss does not hit the target, the student loses the turn.

4. Points can be assigned for each correct answer.

Conclusion	Exercise Set 4.1 in your textbook includes a variety of expressions to evaluate as well as cautions to keep in mind.

Problems	Answers	Problems	Answers
1) Evaluate t^3 when $t = 5$	125	11) $\dfrac{(2y)^9}{(2y)^9}$	1
2) Evaluate $4t^2$ when $t = -3$	36	12) $\dfrac{y^{-2}}{y^{-9}}$	y^7
3) $p^4 p^{12} p^8$	p^{24}	13) $\dfrac{8^{12}}{8^6}$	8^6
4) 3^{-2}	$\dfrac{1}{9}$	14) $a^{11} \cdot a^{-3} \cdot a^{-18}$	$\dfrac{1}{a^{10}}$
5) 2^{-3}	$\dfrac{1}{8}$	15) Evaluate y^{15} when $y = 1$	1
6) $\dfrac{1}{y^{-4}}$	y^4	16) Evaluate $z^5 + 5$ when $z = -2$	-27
7) $3^{-5} \cdot 3^8$	3^3	17) Evaluate $y^2 - 7$ when $y = -10$	93
8) $(8x)^0 (8x)^1$	$8x$	18) Evaluate m^3 when $m = 3$	27
9) $t^8 \cdot t^{-8}$	1	19) $\dfrac{5^8}{5^6}$	5^2
10) $\dfrac{7^5}{7^2}$	7^3	20) $\dfrac{x^{-7}}{x^{-7}}$	1

Activity 4.2   Use exponential and scientific notation to represent job salary.

Focus	Exponential and scientific notation
Time	15–20 minutes
Group size	2
Materials	Calculator
Background	If you were offered a job which paid $1 the first day, $2 the second day, $4 the third day, and so on, would you accept the job? Work through this activity to help you decide. You may be surprised at the result!

1. The salary schedule for this job is given in the table below. On the first day, you will receive $1, on the second day, your salary is doubled to $2, and on the third day, this salary is doubled to $4. On subsequent days, the pattern is continued, with each day's salary double that of the previous day. Complete the table to see what you will earn on each day of the first week (consisting of 5 days).

Day	Salary	Exponential notation
1	$1	2^0
2	$2	2^1
3	$4	
4		
5		
Week 1 total		

Use a calculator to calculate the total salary that you will receive after 5 days. Based on this total, would you accept the job?

2. Now, continue the calculations to figure out how much salary you would receive in the second week (days 6 to 10). Find the total for Week 2, as well as the grand total for both weeks.

Day	Salary	Exponential notation
6		
7		
8		
9		
10		
Week 2 total		
Grand total		

Does the salary package look more attractive now?

3. Continue with the salary calculations for Weeks 3 and 4. Split the work with your partner, so each does one week.

Day	Salary	Exponential notation
11		
12		
13		
14		
15		
Week 3 total		
Grand total		

Day	Salary	Exponential notation
16		
17		
18		
19		
20		
Week 4 total		
Grand total		

4. How does the salary package look now? Would you accept this job? Summarize the salary totals for each of the four weeks in the table below. Use scientific notation to write any amounts that have more than 6 digits.

	Decimal notation	Scientific notation
Week 1 total		
Week 2 total		
Week 3 total		
Week 4 total		
Grand total		

Conclusion	Now that you have done the mathematical calculations, would you accept the job? This activity gives you an example of exponential growth. In this case, an amount grows by doubling the previous amount. Another example of doubling is with cell growth, where each cell grows by dividing into two "daughter" cells. If you continue your study of algebra, you should encounter further examples of exponential growth.

Activity 4.5   Visualize polynomial multiplication using rectangles.

Focus	Polynomial multiplication
Time	15–20 minutes
Group size	2
Background	The product of two binomials can be regarded as the area of a rectangle with width equal to one binomial, and length equal to the other binomial. This activity will help you visualize polynomial multiplication using these rectangles.

1. First, consider the multiplication of the binomials $(x + 3)$ and $(x + 2)$. Each binomial represents one side of a rectangle, as shown below.

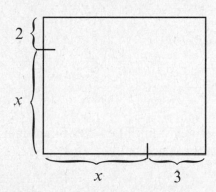

Use a pencil to divide the rectangle into four smaller rectangles by drawing horizontal and vertical lines from the tick marks. Label the rectangles with the letters A, B, C, and D. Then find the area of each rectangle and record your results in the table below.

Rectangle	Length	Width	Area
A			
B			
C			
D			
		Total	

2. Now, multiply the binomials using the distributive property, as described in Section 4.5 of your textbook.

$$(x+3)(x+2) = \underline{\hspace{4cm}}$$

Compare this answer with your total area from the table. Do they match? If not, check your work and correct any errors.

3. Now that you have seen how to represent polynomial multiplication using rectangles, practice the concept with your partner. Choose two binomials of the form

$$(x + \underline{\hspace{1.5cm}})(x + \underline{\hspace{1.5cm}})$$

One group member draws the rectangle as shown in step 1, then finds the total area of all four rectangles. Write your answer in the space below.

The other group member multiplies the binomials using the distributive property. Write your answer in the space below.

Compare answers, and correct any errors.

4. Create another binomial multiplication problem, and repeat step 3, but switch roles. The first group member now multiplies the binomials using the distributive property, while the second group member finds the product by drawing rectangles.

   As before, compare answers and correct any errors.

Conclusion	This activity gives you a visual representation of polynomial multiplication. This representation will also be used in Section 9.2 when we visualize completion of the square as a method for solving quadratic equations.

Activity 4.6   Derive the special product formulas.

Focus	Special Products
Time	15–20 minutes
Group size	2
Background	Two binomials can always be multiplied using the distributive property. However, for binomials that are of a certain form, the special product formulas may be used as a shortcut.

1. Multiply the following binomials using the distributive property. One group member should do the computations in Table 1, while the other group member does the computations in Table 2. Do your scratch work on a separate sheet of paper, and just write down the final products in the appropriate spaces in the table. The first problem has been done as an example.

Table 1

$(x+1)^2 = (x+1)(x+1) =$	x^2	+	2	x	+	1
$(x+2)^2 = (x+2)(x+2) =$	x^2	+		x	+	
$(x+3)^2 = (x+3)(x+3) =$	x^2	+		x	+	
$(x+4)^2 = (x+4)(x+4) =$	x^2	+		x	+	

Table 2

$(x-1)^2 = (x-1)(x-1)$	x^2	–	2	x	+	1
$(x-2)^2 = (x-2)(x-2) =$	x^2	–		x	+	
$(x-3)^2 = (x-3)(x-3) =$	x^2	–		x	+	
$(x-4)^2 = (x-4)(x-4) =$	x^2	–		x	+	

2. Look at the results in your tables. Can you see a pattern in the coefficients of x and in the constant terms? In your own words, describe your observations.

3. Based on your observations, write down the product of the two binomials given below, __without__ using the distributive property.

$$(x+7)(x+7) = \underline{\hspace{4cm}}$$

Now, notice that the multiplication above can be written as the square of a binomial. Complete the blanks below.

$$(x+7)(x+7) = (\underline{\hspace{2cm}})^2 = \underline{\hspace{4cm}}$$

4. Finally, write down the final product of each of the following binomial squares, __without__ using the distributive property. Follow the pattern from step 4.

$$(x+6)^2 =$$

$$(x-6)^2 =$$

$$(x-9)^2 =$$

5. Now, let's extend the results you have so far. Follow the procedure outlined in step 1, and multiply the binomials in Tables 3 and 4 using the distributive property. One group member should do the computations in Table 3, while the other group member does the computations in Table 4. Do your scratch work on a separate sheet of paper, and just write down the final answers in the appropriate spaces in the table

Table 3

$(2x+1)^2 = (2x+1)(2x+1) =$	4	x^2	+	4	x	+	1
$(2x+3)^2 = (2x+3)(2x+3) =$		x^2	+		x	+	
$(3x+2)^2 = (3x+2)(3x+2) =$		x^2	+		x	+	
$(3x+4)^2 = (3x+4)(3x+4) =$		x^2	+		x	+	

Table 4

$(2x-1)^2 = (2x-1)(2x-1) =$	4	x^2	–	4	x	+	1
$(2x-3)^2 = (2x-3)(2x-3) =$		x^2	–		x	+	
$(3x-2)^2 = (3x-2)(3x-2) =$		x^2	–		x	+	
$(3x-4)^2 = (3x-4)(3x-4) =$		x^2	–		x	+	

6. Analyze the results in the tables. In your own words, write down the pattern that you observe.

Use the pattern to multiply the following binomials <u>without</u> using the distributive property.

$(2x+5)^2 =$

$(5x-6)^2 =$

$(4x-9)^2 =$

7. In the space below, write down the special product formulas from Section 4.6 in your textbook.

$(A+B)^2 =$
$(A-B)^2 =$

Compare these formulas with the pattern you wrote down in step 6. Can you see how the formulas are the algebraic equivalent of your observations?

Conclusion	This activity should give you a better understanding of two of the special product formulas. While you can always multiply binomials using the distributive property, the formulas provide a shortcut for the multiplication. They will also prove useful when you need to factor trinomials in the next chapter.

Activity 4.8   Tic-Tac-Oh!

Focus	Division of Polynomials
Time	15 minutes
Group size	2
Materials	Draw a tic-tac-toe design on the board, marker, 9 problems (with answers)
Background	You will need to recall long division as it is performed in arithmetic. When we divide, we repeat the following procedure: divide, multiply, subtract, and bring down the next term.

1. Draw a tic-tac-toe design on the board numbered 1–9 left-to-right.

2. The student, chosen by the instructor, chooses one of the problems, which have been numbered 1–9, and carries out the division.

3. If the division is done correctly, then "O" is placed on that square. If the problem is answered incorrectly, then "X" is placed on that square.

4. The winner needs to have three "O's" horizontally, vertically or diagonally.

Conclusion	Exercise Set 4.8 in your textbook includes a variety of exercises that will give you practice with dividing a polynomial by a monomial and dividing a polynomial by a divisor that is a binomial.

Problems	Answers
1) $(2x^3 + 6x^2 + 4x) \div (2x)$	$x^2 + 3x + 2$
2) $\dfrac{2x^4 y^6 - 3x^3 y^4 + 5x^2 y^3}{x^2 y^2}$	$2x^2 y^4 - 3xy^2 + 5y$
3) $(x^2 + x - 6) \div (x + 3)$	$x - 2$
4) $(x^2 + 2x - 8) \div (x - 2)$	$x + 4$
5) $(15t^3 + 24t^2 - 6t) \div (3t)$	$5t^2 + 8t - 2$
6) $(x^2 + 4x + 4) \div (x + 2)$	$x + 2$
7) $\dfrac{x^2 - 9}{x - 3}$	$x + 3$
8) $(x^2 - 6x + 9) \div (x - 3)$	$x - 3$
9) $\dfrac{8x^3 - 22x^2 - 5x + 12}{4x + 3}$	$2x^2 - 7x + 4$

Activity 5.1   Chair Basketball Relay

Focus	Introduction to Factoring
Time	30 minutes
Group size	2 teams of however many students
Materials	2 chairs (1 for each team, 2 small basketballs, 1 small basketball hoop [can be purchased at toy shops]), a list of problems—enough for the size of the group.
Background	Introduce factoring with a review of factoring natural numbers.

1. Set up the basketball hoop in the front of the room.

2. The chairs are set at an appropriate distance from the hoop.

3. Students are divided into 2 teams; they toss a coin to see which team will go first, and they line up behind their chair. The first member of each team sits in the chair.

4. A problem is posed to the student in the chair. If the student answers correctly, the team receives 1 point. S/he can then try to toss the basketball in the hoop. If it lands in the hoop, the team is awarded 2 extra points. Then the first student from the other team is given the next problem.

   If the student does not answer correctly, the team scores 0 and the question goes to the other team.

   As each student answers, he/she moves to the back of the line.

5. Play will continue until all questions are answered correctly. The winning team gets a treat.

Conclusion	Exercise Set 5.1 in your textbook includes a variety of problems: finding the GCF; factoring polynomials when the terms have a common factor; factoring out the greatest common factor; and factoring certain expressions with four terms using factoring by grouping.

Problems	Answers
1) Factor: $3x + 6$	$3(x+2)$
2) Multiply: $2x(x^2 + 5x + 4)$	$2x^3 + 10x^2 + 8x$
3) Factor: $2x^3 + 10x^2 + 8x$	$2x(x^2 + 5x + 4)$
4) Factor: $x^2 + 3x$	$x(x+3)$
5) Factor: $9x^4y^2 - 15x^3y + 3x^2y$	$3x^2y(3x^2y - 5x + 1)$
6) Factor: $35x^7 - 49x^6 + 14x^5 - 63x^3$	$7x^3(5x^4 - 7x^3 + 2x^2 - 9)$
7) Factor: $x^2(x+7) + 3(x+7)$	$(x^2 + 3)(x+7)$
8) Factor: $x^2(a+b) + 2(a+b)$	$(x^2 + 2)(a+b)$
9) Factor by grouping: $x^3 + 7x^2 + 3x + 21$	$(x^2 + 3)(x+7)$
10) Factor by grouping: $8t^3 + 2t^2 + 12t + 3$	$(2t^2 + 3)(4t + 1)$
11) Factor: $8x^4 + 24x^2$	$8x^2(x^2 + 3)$
12) Factor: $5a^3(2a-7) - (2a-7)$	$(5a^3 - 1)(2a - 7)$
13) Factor: $3z^2(2z+1) + (2z+1)$	$(3z^2 + 1)(2z + 1)$
14) Factor: $m^4(8-3m) - 7(8-3m)$	$(m^4 - 7)(8 - 3m)$
15) Factor by grouping: $x^3 + 3x^2 + 2x + 6$	$(x^2 + 2)(x+3)$
16) Factor by grouping: $6z^3 + 3z^2 + 2z + 1$	$(3z^2 + 1)(2z + 1)$
17) Factor by grouping: $8x^3 - 12x^2 + 6x - 9$	$(4x^2 + 3)(2x - 3)$

Introductory Algebra   Collaborative Learning Activities

Problems	Answers
18) Factor by grouping: $7x^3 - 14x^2 - x + 2$	$(7x^2 - 1)(x - 2)$
19) Factor by grouping: $2x^3 - 8x^2 - 9x + 36$	$(2x^2 - 9)(x - 4)$
20) Factor by grouping: $2x^3 + 6x^2 + x + 3$	$(2x^2 + 1)(x + 3)$

Activity 5.2   Hole-in-One Factoring

Focus	Factoring Trinomials of the Type $x^2 + bx + c$
Time	20–30 minutes
Group size	2
Materials	Miniature golf club and golf ball, empty can (4–6 inch diameter), 6 problems for each game.
Background	Factor polynomials when the terms have a common factor, factoring out the greatest common factor.

1. Tape off 6 areas (about 10 inches between each area) with masking tape.

2. Put empty can on its side (about 10 inches from the first line).

3. The team member answers as many of the 6 questions as possible in 5 minutes.

4. Rubric: 0 questions answered correctly: Putt from behind the first line.

    1 question answered correctly: Putt from behind second line.

    2 questions answered correctly: Putt from behind third line.

    .
    .
    .

    6 questions answered correctly: Putt from behind the seventh line.

5. One point is given for each question that is answered correctly and five bonus points for putting the golf ball in the can.

Conclusion	Exercise Set 5.2 in your textbook includes a variety of equations factoring $x^2 + bx + c$ when c is positive and factoring $x^2 + bx + c$ when c is negative.

Game 1

Problems	Answers
1) Factor: $x^2 + 8x + 15$	$(x+3)(x+5)$
2) Factor: $x^2 + 5x + 6$	$(x+2)(x+3)$
3) Factor: $x^2 + 7x + 12$	$(x+3)(x+4)$
4) Factor: $x^2 - 5x - 14$	$(x+2)(x-7)$
5) Factor: $z^2 - 8z + 7$	$(z-1)(z-7)$
6) Factor: $a^2 + 7a - 30$	$(a+10)(a-3)$

Game 2

Problems	Answers
1) Factor: $d^2 - 7d + 10$	$(d-2)(d-5)$
2) Factor: $x^2 - 4x - 21$	$(x-7)(x+3)$
3) Factor: $x^2 - 7x - 18$	$(x-9)(x+2)$
4) Factor: $x^2 + x - 42$	$(x-6)(x+7)$
5) Factor: $x^2 + 20x + 100$	$(x+10)^2$
6) Factor: $x^2 + 2x - 15$	$(x-3)(x+5)$

Activity 5.3   Go Factor!

Focus	Factoring Trinomials $ax^2 + bx + c$, a does not $= 1$: The FOIL Method
Time	20–30 minutes
Group size	2
Materials	20 rectangular cards (10 cards with trinomials and 10 cards with factored answers)
Background	In section 5.2, we learned a trial-and-error method to factor trinomials of the type $x^2 + bx + c$. In this section, we factor trinomials in which the coefficient of the leading term x^2 is not 1. The procedure we learn is a refined trial-and error method.

1. Mix the 20 cards and pass out 5 cards (alternating) each to the team members. The remaining cards are placed face-down in the middle.

2. If the member has a pair (Trinomial and factored answer), then the pair is put face-up on the table. If the member does not have a pair, then another card is taken from the top of the pile.

3. Play continues until a player has put down all of the cards or all cards in the middle are gone.

4. Winner has the most pairs.

Conclusion	Exercise Set 5.3 in your text book includes one of the two ways to factor general trinomials. Section 5.4 will demonstrate the "ac" method. The student can use the method he or she prefers.

$2x^2 - 7x - 4$	$5x^2 - x - 18$
$9x^2 + 18x - 16$	$12x^2 + 31x + 20$
$6x^2 + 23x + 7$	$4x^2 + 4x - 15$
$14x^2 + 19x - 3$	$3x^2 - 4x + 1$
$2x^2 - x - 1$	$9x^2 - 42x + 49$

$(3x - 2)(3x + 8)$	$(2x + 1)(x - 4)$
$(3x + 4)(4x + 5)$	$(5x + 9)(x - 2)$
$(7x - 1)(2x + 3)$	$(3x + 1)(2x + 7)$
$(3x - 1)(x - 1)$	$(2x - 3)(2x + 5)$
$(3x - 7)^2$	$(2x + 1)(x - 1)$

Activity 5.5   Take 4 and Double it.

Focus	Factoring Trinomial Squares and Differences of Squares.
Time	15–25 minutes
Group size	3
Materials	White board or chalk board on which to put the 4 problems and 4 papers with answers with sticky tape on the back of each.
Background	This activity provides continued practice with factoring trinomials.

1. Four Trinomial Squares/Differences of Squares are written on the white board or chalk board.

2. The four answers are printed on paper with sticky tape on the back.

3. The student has 10 seconds to place the answers under the problem on the board.

4. Rubric: 0 right = 0 points

                   1 right = 1 point

                   2 right = 2 points

                   3 right = 4 points

                   4 right = 8 points

5. Winner has the most points.

Conclusion	The student should recognize and factor trinomial squares and factor differences of squares, taking care to factor completely.

Problems on board	Answers on sticky paper
Factor:	
1) $x^2 - 14x + 49$	$(x-7)^2$
2) $x^2 - 2x + 1$	$(x-1)^2$
3) $x^2 + 2x + 1$	$(x+1)^2$
4) $x^2 + 14x + 49$	$(x+7)^2$

Problems on board	Answers on sticky paper
Factor:	
1) $16x^2 - 9$	$(4x+3)(4x-3)$
2) $25x^2 - 4$	$(5x+2)(5x-2)$
3) $4x^2 - 25$	$(2x+5)(2x-5)$
4) $9x^2 - 16$	$(3x+4)(3x-4)$

Activity 5.6   Create polynomials for factoring.

Focus	Factoring polynomials
Time	15–20 minutes
Group size	4
Background	Achieving mastery with polynomial factoring takes practice, especially when all types of factoring exercises are mixed together. Follow the steps given in Section 5.6 of your textbook to help you factor the polynomials in this activity.

1. First, each group member makes up two binomials and multiplies them together. Choose binomials that have integer coefficients, like $2x - 5$ or $x + 3$. You can also choose one of the special products. Write down the binomials below, and multiply them.

2. On a separate sheet of paper, write down the product of the binomials; <u>do not write down the binomials.</u> Pass the paper to the group member on your left.

3. In the space below, write down the polynomial you receive. Factor the polynomial and write down your factors in the right column.

Polynomial	Factors

4. Pass the polynomial to the group member on your left, and repeat step 3. Continue until all group members have factored all polynomials.

5. Compare your results with the rest of your group. Discuss any differences, and check all factorizations by multiplying.

6. If there is time, repeat steps 1 through 5, and make up a different problem for the rest of the group to factor. Pass the polynomial around to all group members as before, and factor the polynomials you receive. Compare results at the end, and make sure all group members understand the reasons for the correct answers.

Polynomial	Factors

Conclusion	The act of creating a polynomial that can be factored helps you gain a better understanding of the factoring procedure. It is also important to realize that any factorization can be checked by multiplying.

Activity 5.7   Create and solve quadratic equations as a group.

Focus	Solving quadratic equations
Time	20-25 minutes
Group size	4
Background	Solving quadratic equations is an important skill in algebra. This activity will give you practice in using the principle of zero products to solve quadratic equations.

1. Each group will create and solve quadratic equations by following the steps outlined below. Study the example so you understand the mechanics of this process.

	Example	
Step 1	The first group member thinks of two numbers and writes x=one number or x=another number, on a piece of notebook paper, and passes the paper to the second group member.	$4; -3$ $x = 4$ or $x = -3$
Step 2	The second group member creates two binomials that will give the solutions from step 1. Write the binomials as a product, and set the product equal to zero. Write the new equation below the first ones, and pass the paper to the third group member.	$(x-4)(x+3) = 0$
Step 3	The third group member multiplies the two binomials, writes the new equation below the second one, and folds over the paper so that only the last equation is shown. He or she then passes the paper to the fourth group member.	$x^2 - x - 12 = 0$
Step 4	The fourth group member writes the equation on his or her record sheet, and solves the equation. When done, the group unfolds the notebook paper and checks that the solution matches the two numbers written by the first group member. If it does not, the group should find out where the mistake occurred.	$x^2 - x - 12 = 0$ $(x-4)(x+3) = 0$ $x-4 = 0$ or $x+3 = 0$ $x = 4$ or $x = -3$

RECORD SHEET

ROUND 1 Equation:

     Solution:

ROUND 2 Equation:

     Solution:

ROUND 3 Equation:

     Solution:

2. Now you are ready to create your own equations. In Round 1, use only positive integers in step 1.

Each group member begins with step 1, writing down the equation on a piece of notebook paper. He or she then passes the paper to the group member on his or her right.

Modify the equation you receive according to step 2, then pass the paper to your right again. Continue until you reach step 4; you should have an equation that looks like $ax^2 + bx + c = 0$. Write down this equation on the record sheet on the previous page. Then, solve and check the equation, following the directions for step 4.

When all group members are done, examine all four equations in your group and correct any errors.

3. For Round 2, you may use negative integers to create the solutions in step 1. Start with a fresh sheet of notebook paper and pass the equation around the group as before.

4. Round 3 gets a little more complicated, as you may use fractions for the two solutions in step 1.

| Conclusion | Notice that you are writing equivalent equations in steps 2 and 3. This is one of the fundamental concepts in equation solving, as explained in Chapter 2 of your textbook. This activity should give you a clearer understanding of how the principle of zero products works and consequently increase your proficiency in solving quadratic equations. |

Activity 6.7   Develop a formula for calculating the time required to complete a task when working together.

Focus	Formulas, work problems
Time	15–20 minutes
Group size	2
Background	Solving formulas is one of the more useful algebraic skills. This activity will lead you through an intuitive development of a formula for calculating the time required for two people to complete a task working together.

1. Use the method shown in Section 6.7 of your textbook to calculate the time required to complete a task working together, for the individual times given in the table below. Leave your answers in fraction notation.

    Split the work with your partner, so each does two problems.

Time required for first worker	Time required for second worker	Time required working together
2	3	
2	5	
3	4	
3	5	

2. Study the numerator of each answer. Can you see a connection between the individual times and the numerator? State this relationship in your own words.

    Now study the denominator of each answer. What is the relationship between the individual times and the denominator?

In your own words, complete the formula below, using the relationships you wrote for the numerator and denominator.

Time required working together= _____

3. Use the formula above to solve the following problem.

How long would it take two people to complete a task if each person takes 4 hours and 5 hours to do the job individually?

Test your formula by using the method shown in the textbook to solve the problem. If necessary, modify your formula so the answers match.

4. Now, let's write the formula using algebraic symbols. Suppose one person takes a hours to complete a task alone, and a second person takes b hours to complete the same task alone. Let t represent the time it would take both people to complete the task working together. Follow the formula developed in step 2, and write an algebraic formula for the time required working together.

$t =$ _____

5. From Section 6.7 of your textbook, the equation used to solve work problems is

$$\frac{t}{a} + \frac{t}{b} = 1$$

Using the methods shown in Section 6.7 of your textbook, solve the equation for the variable t.

Compare your solution with the formula you developed in step 4. Are they identical? Discuss any discrepancies with your partner. If necessary, check your work with that of another group, and try to resolve any differences.

Conclusion	You can use the work formula developed in this activity to solve work problems from Section 6.7 of your textbook. The skills developed here can also be used when solving other formulas in your textbook.

Section 7.3   Compare the three methods for solving systems of equations in two variables.

Focus	Solving systems of equations
Time	20–25 minutes
Group size	3
Background	There are three methods for solving a system of two equations: graphing, substitution, and elimination. In this activity, all three methods will be used to solve each system. The solutions will be compared, and criteria will be established to help you decide which method is preferable for each problem.

1. Tear out the three pages labeled Systems A, B, and C, and distribute one page to each group member. Begin by solving your system using the graphing method. Show your work on the page, and draw the graphs on the grid provided. Neatly organize and label your work, so the other group members can follow your steps.

2. When all group members are done, pass your paper to the group member on your left. Solve the system you receive using the substitution method. Show your work in the space provided. Again, be neat and organized so the other group members can follow your steps.

3. Finally, pass your paper to the group member on your left, and this time, solve the system using the elimination method.

4. When all group members are finished, study the three methods used to solve each system. Decide as a group what the preferred method or methods are for each system, and fill in the following table. Briefly state a reason for your group's choices.

System	Preferred method(s)	Reason
A		
B		
C		

5. Discuss your choices with another group. Do both groups agree on the preferred method(s) for solving each system? Decide whether there is a "right" and "wrong" method for solving any system.

Conclusion	Use the criteria you established in step 4 to help you decide which method to use when solving a system of two equations. While it may be easier to rely always on one method, it is a good idea to be versatile and use different methods as appropriate.

SYSTEM A

$$3x + 2y = 8,$$
$$5x - 3y = 7$$

GRAPHING METHOD

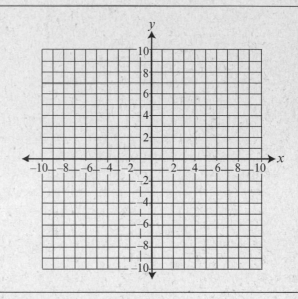

SUBSTITUTION METHOD

ELIMINATION METHOD

SYSTEM B

$$x + y = 4,$$
$$2x - y = 5$$

GRAPHING METHOD	
	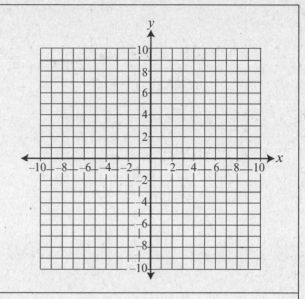

SUBSTITUTION METHOD	ELIMINATION METHOD

SYSTEM C $5x - y = 7,$
$3x + 2y = 12$

GRAPHING METHOD

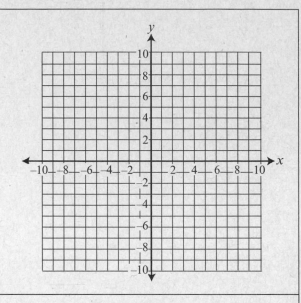

SUBSTITUTION METHOD

ELIMINATION METHOD

Introductory Algebra   Collaborative Learning Activities

Section 7.4   Model a consumer problem using a system of equations.

Focus	Applications of systems of equations
Time	20–25 minutes
Group size	3
Background	With the advent of deregulation of the cellular phone industry, there has been a surge in the number of companies offering cellular service nationwide. Consumers are faced with many choices of rate plans. This activity will provide you with a mathematical tool for analyzing the rate plans from three different companies.

The rate plans for three cellular phone companies are listed below.

Company	Monthly service fee	Cost per minute
AQQ Wireless	$19.99	$0.75
GGG Mobilnet	$23.95	$0.36
Fast PDQ	$29.99	$0.19

1. Each group member should select a different company listed in the table. Write an equation that represents the monthly cost in terms of the number of minutes. Then use this equation to calculate the total monthly cost for your company's rate plan for the given talk times.

COMPANY:	
EQUATION:	
Talk time, in minutes	Monthly cost
15	
30	
45	
60	

2. Next, use the grid on the next page to draw the graph representing the monthly cost for each company. Let the horizontal axis represent the talk time, in minutes, and let the vertical axis represent the monthly cost for each plan. Decide as a group how many minutes or dollars each square should represent. Label each axis clearly, and make the graphs as neat as possible.

3. Using the graphs from step 2, the group member who selected AQQ plan should determine what talk time would result in the same monthly cost as the GGG plan. Round your answer to the nearest minute. Alternatively, find this talk time by solving the system of equations formed by the two equations representing the AQQ plan and the GGG plan.

   Similarly, the group member who selected the GGG plan should determine when the monthly cost would be the same as the PDQ plan. Finally, the group member who selected the PDQ plan should determine when this monthly cost would equal AQQ's cost.

   Organize your results using the table below. Ignore the boxes that are shaded. Notice that the values for the three boxes to the right of the shaded boxes are identical to the corresponding values for the boxes to the left of the shaded boxes.

	AQQ	GGG	PDQ
AQQ	███████		
GGG		███████	
PDQ			███████

4. Now, use the graph to decide which plan would have the lowest monthly cost for the talk times listed below. Use the table to decide which plan you would choose if you wanted to purchase cellular service.

Talk time, in minutes	Least expensive plan
15	
30	
45	
60	

Conclusion	Algebraic and graphical analysis of a problem can provide you with useful information when making choices. Follow the model given in this activity when you need to make consumer decisions in the future.

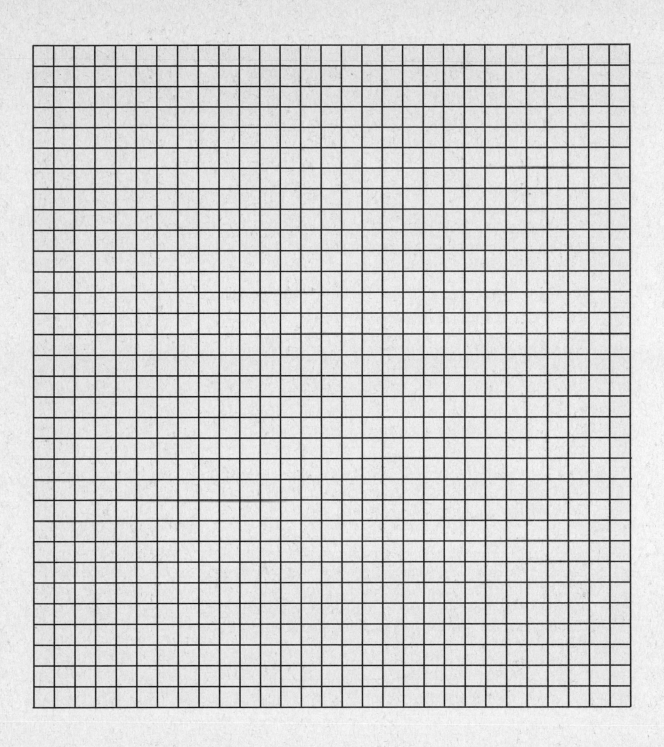

Activity 8.1   Develop a formula for the swing time of a pendulum.

Focus	Square roots, formulas
Time	25–30 minutes
Group size	3
Materials	Tape measure, watch or clock to measure time in seconds, pendulum (see below), calculator
Background	A pendulum is simply a string, a rope, or a chain with a weight of some sort attached at one end. When the unweighted end is held, a pendulum can swing freely from side to side. A shoe hanging from a shoelace, a yo-yo, a pendant hanging from a chain, a fishing weight hanging from a fish line, or a hair brush tied to a length of dental floss are all examples of a pendulum. In this activity, each group will develop a mathematical model or formula that relates a pendulum's length L to the time T that it takes for one complete swing back and forth (one "cycle)

1. Make a pendulum by attaching a weight to one end of a string. The size of the weight is unimportant; it should be heavy enough so the pendulum swings smoothly, but not so heavy that the string would break.

2. One group member holds the string so that its length is 1 foot. A second group member should lift the weight to one side and then release it; do not throw the weight. It does not matter how high you lift the weight. The third group member should determine the time, in seconds, for one complete swing (cycle), by timing <u>five</u> cycles and dividing the time by 5. Record this time in the table below.

   Repeat this procedure for each length listed in the table.

Length, L (in feet)	Time, T (in seconds)
1	
1.5	
2	
2.5	
3	
3.5	

3. Examine the table your group has created. Can you find a number, *a*, such that $T \approx aL$ for all pairs of values in the table?

$$T \approx \underline{\hspace{2cm}} \cdot L$$

4. To see if a better model can be found, add a third column to the table and fill in $\sqrt{L}$ for each value of *L* listed. Copy the times from the table in step 1.

L	$\sqrt{L}$	T
1		
1.5		
2		
2.5		
3		
3.5		

Can you find a number, *b*, such that $T \approx b\sqrt{L}$? Does this appear to be a more accurate model than $T \approx aL$?

$$T \approx \underline{\hspace{2cm}} \cdot \sqrt{L}$$

5. Use the model from step 3 to predict the time for one complete cycle when the string is 4 feet long. Then check your prediction by measuring *T as* you did in step 1. Was your prediction "acceptable"? Compare your results with those of another group.

6. In Section 9.4 of your textbook, there is a formula relating *T* and *L, as* stated below.

$$T = 2\pi\sqrt{\frac{L}{32}} = \frac{2\pi}{\sqrt{32}} \cdot \sqrt{L}$$

Use a calculator to figure out the decimal equivalent of $2\pi/\sqrt{32}$. Rewrite the above formula using this number.

$$T \approx \underline{\hspace{2cm}} \cdot \sqrt{L}$$

How does the value of *b* from step 3 compare with the decimal equivalent of $2\pi/\sqrt{32}$?

Conclusion	The formula you developed that relates the pendulum's length to the swing time is know as an <u>empirical</u> formula, since it was derived from experimental data. The <u>theoretical</u> formula in step 5 is obtained by applying physics principles to the situation. Both approaches are important in the study of physics.

Activity 8.6   Use the Pythagorean Theorem to draw a rectangle.

Focus	Pythagorean Theorem
Time	15–20 minutes
Group size	3–4
Materials	Tape measure, masking tape, string, scissors, calculator
Background	The Pythagorean Theorem gives the relationship for the sides of a right triangle. This formula can also be used to measure a 90° angle. In this activity, you will measure 90° angles and draw a rectangle using the Pythagorean Theorem.

1. First, draw a right triangle in the space below and label its sides using the letters *a, b,* and *c.* Then write down the Pythagorean Theorem for your triangle in the space below.

2. The project is to use string and a tape measure to draw a rectangle. Decide on the dimensions for your rectangle, and sketch it below.

Length = _____

Width = _____

Next, choose a clear area on the floor or wall to draw the rectangle. Use masking tape so you won't permanently mark up the surface.

Measure out the length of the rectangle and draw it with masking tape. It does not matter where you position this side.

3. The width of the rectangle must be drawn at a right angle to the masking tape. In order to do this, you must be able to accurately measure the angle. You will use the Pythagorean Theorem for this part. First, use the Pythagorean Theorem to calculate the length of the diagonal of your rectangle. Show your work in the space below.

4. Next, cut one piece of string equal to the width of your rectangle. Cut a second piece of string equal to the length of the diagonal.

   One group member takes the "width" string and holds one end to the left side of the masking tape. Another group member holds one end of the "diagonal" string to the right of the masking tape. The third group member takes the free ends of each string and brings them together. Lay the strings flat on the floor (or wall) and pull them firmly so there is no slack.

   Mark the point where they meet; this will be the top left corner of the rectangle. Use masking tape to draw the width of the rectangle from the bottom left to the top left.

5. Repeat this procedure, but switch the positions of the "width" and "diagonal" strings. This will give you the top right corner of the rectangle. Draw the width of the rectangle, using masking tape again, from the bottom right to the top right.

6. Check the accuracy of your right angles by measuring the top length of the rectangle. Does this measurement equal the length of the bottom side?

7. Go around the room and look at the rectangles drawn by the other groups. Check their work by measuring the width, length, and diagonal. See if these dimensions satisfy the Pythagorean Theorem.

8. When the class has completed this activity, remove all masking tape from the floor and walls!

Conclusion	Builders and construction workers regularly use the Pythagorean Theorem to lay out a right angle. Typically, they use the 3-4-5 triangle, since $3^2 + 4^2 = 5^2$, and these numbers are easy to memorize.

Activity 9.2   Visualize completion of the square using rectangles.

Focus	Completing the square
Time	15–20 minutes
Group size	2
Materials	Ruler
Background	In Activity 4.5, polynomial multiplication was represented by the area of a rectangle. This activity uses the same visual representation to explain the rule for completing the square.

1. Recall, from Activity 4.5, that the product of the binomials $x+3$ and $x+2$ can be represented as the area of a rectangle, as shown below.

Algebraically, the product is found as follows.

$$(x+3)(x+2) = x^2 + 3x + 2x + 6$$
$$= x^2 + 5x + 6$$

Notice that the middle term, $5x$, is represented by two rectangles with areas $3x$ and $2x$.

2. Now, consider the polynomial $x^2 + 6x$. Study the sequence below to see how to complete the square using rectangles. First, draw a square and rectangle to represent $x^2 + 6x$.

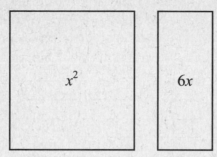

Divide the rectangle into two equal rectangles, each with an area of $3x$.

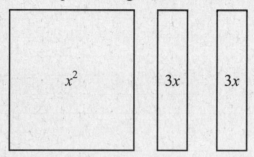

Now, move one of the rectangles so it sits on top of the square.

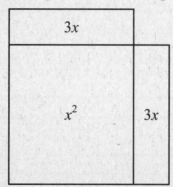

Notice that there is a "hole" in the top right corner of the diagram. Also, note that the length and width of the rectangle are equal to x+3, so the rectangle is actually a square. To fill in the hole, we need a square with dimensions of 3 by 3, thus with an area of 9.

We have, literally, "completed the square". Algebraically, the polynomial has become $x^2 + 6x + 9$.

3. Now, you practice completing the square. Draw a sequence of four figures, similar to those shown on the previous page, to complete the square for the polynomial $x^2 + 8x$. Group members should take turns, so that each member draws and labels two figures.

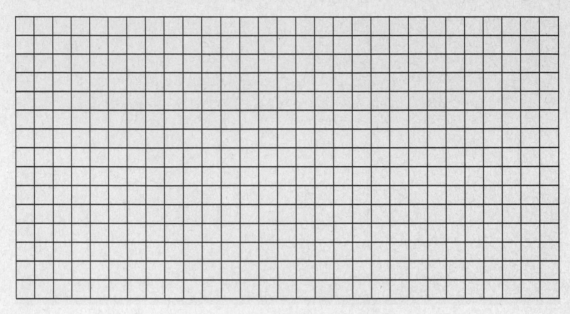

4. Repeat the previous step to complete the square for the polynomial $x^2 + 14x$. The group member who drew the first drawing in step 3 should take the second turn this time.

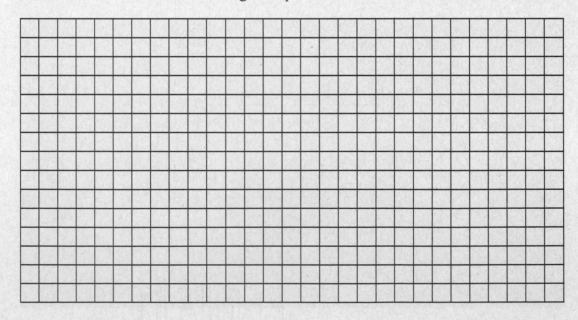

Conclusion	This activity shows you a concrete representation of the procedure for completing the square. As you saw, the name "completing the square" literally comes from the step where a missing piece is needed to make a complete square. Knowing this should give you a better understanding of the procedure.

Activity 9.6   Practice graphing and identifying the graphs of quadratic equations.

Focus	Graphs of quadratic equations
Time	20–25 minutes
Group size	4
Background	It is important not only to be able to graph quadratic equations, but also to be able to match a graph with the appropriate equation. This activity will give you practice graphing and identifying the graphs of quadratic equations.
Instructor notes	This activity can also be done with a graphing calculator.

1. Each group member should select a different one of the following sets of equations.

<table>
<tr>
<td>A:</td>
<td>

$y = x^2 + 2$

$y = x^2 + 4$

$y = x^2 - 2$

$y = x^2 - 4$
</td>
</tr>
<tr>
<td>B:</td>
<td>

$y = x^2$

$y = 2x^2$

$y = -x^2$

$y = -2x^2$
</td>
</tr>
<tr>
<td>C:</td>
<td>

$y = (x-2)^2$

$y = (x-4)^2$

$y = (x+2)^2$

$y = (x+4)^2$
</td>
</tr>
<tr>
<td>D:</td>
<td>

$y = x^2 + 3x + 2$

$y = x^2 + 2x - 3$

$y = -x^2 - 2x + 3$
</td>
</tr>
</table>

2. Working independently, each group member should graph the set of equations he or she has selected. Use the grid on the next page. <u>Do not</u> label the graphs with their corresponding equations, but instead list the equations on the top of the page in the space provided.

3. After all group members have completed step 2, the graphs should be passed, clockwise, to the person on the left. This group member should then attempt to match each equation with the appropriate graph. If no graph appears to be appropriate, discuss the relevant equation with the group member who drew the graphs. If necessary, ask another group member for guidance in identifying the graphs.

4. Once all equations and graphs have been matched, share your answers with the rest of the group. Make sure everyone agrees on all of the matches.

   Discuss with the group the characteristics you observed while you were graphing your set of equations. Generalize your observations, and write them in your own words in the space below.

Conclusion	While you still need to plot points to get an accurate graph, the skills learned in this activity can help you make a quick check when graphing quadratic equations.

Set _____	Equations:

Introductory Algebra   Collaborative Learning Activities

Activity Appendix E   Perform a statistical analysis of pulse rates.

Focus	Averages, medians, and modes
Time	15–20 minutes
Group size	5
Materials	Stopwatch, calculator
Background	The definitions of average, median, and mode are relatively straightforward. In this activity, you will gather data on pulse rates, and analyze the data by calculating the average, median, and mode.

1. First, locate your pulse. There are two places you can most easily find it. The first, called the **radial** pulse, is located on your wrist. Turn your palm up, and place the forefinger of your other hand on your wrist below the base of your thumb.

   The second pulse, called the **carotid** pulse, is on the side of your throat below the jaw bone under your ear. Again, use your forefinger to locate this pulse.

   Once you have found your pulse, decide which one is easier to find. Then use this location for the remainder of this activity.

2. Each group member will count his or her pulse rate under three different conditions - resting, exercise, and recovery.

   Rest for about 2 minutes, then find your pulse and count the number of beats in a 15 second period. Multiply this number by 4 to get your resting pulse rate in beats per minute. Record this number in the table on the next page. Use one table for all the members of your group.

3. Next, measure your exercise pulse rate. Run in place for 1 minute, then immediately count your pulse for a 15 second period. Multiply this number by 4 to get your exercise pulse rate. Record this number in the appropriate column in the table on the next page.

4. Finally, measure your recovery pulse rate. Rest for about 3 minutes, then measure your pulse rate as you did the previous two times. Record this number in the table as well.

After all group members have recorded their pulse rates in the table, each group should write their pulse rate data on the board, following the same format from the table.

Name	Resting Pulse	Exercise Pulse	Recovery Pulse
AVERAGE			
MEDIAN			
MODE			

5. Now, each group will analyze their group's pulse rate data. Calculate the average, median, and mode for each of the three different pulse rates. Write your results in the appropriate spaces in the table above. Then calculate the average, median, and mode for the class pulse rate data on the board.

6. How does your group's average compare with the class average?

Which average do you think is more representative of the population as a whole? Why do you believe this is so?

7. Compare the median and mode for your group's pulse rates with the class median and mode. Is there a large difference between the two sets of numbers?

Why do you think this is so?

Look up the definitions of median and mode in Appendix E of your textbook. Do the definitions explain the differences in the results? How?

Conclusion	This activity gives you practice in analyzing data using average, median, and mode. As you probably discovered, the larger the data set, the more representative of the population are the results of the analysis. Small data sets may give you an inaccurate picture.